SUPERSPILL

An Account of the 1978 Grounding at Bird Rocks

SUPERSPILL

An Account of the 1978 Grounding at Bird Rocks

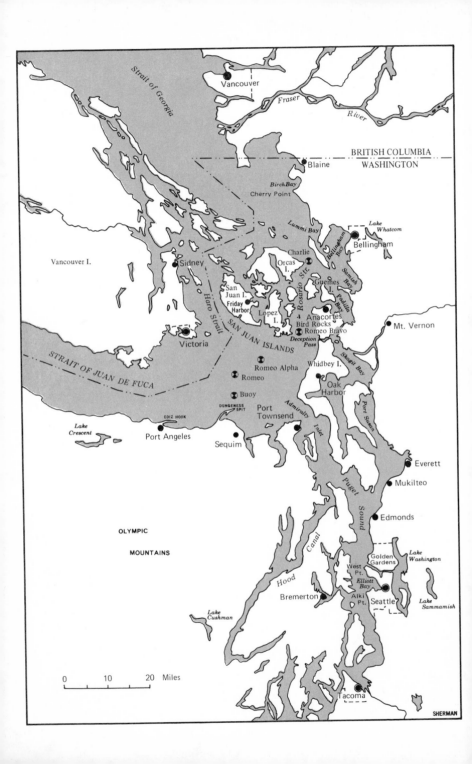

SUPERSPILL

An Account of the
1978 Grounding at Bird Rocks

By
MARY KAY BECKER
and
PATRICIA COBURN

Madrona Press • Seattle

Madrona Press
113 Madrona Place East
Seattle, Washington 98112

FOR

PUGET SOUND

Bird Rocks, consisting of three rocks close together, are almost in the middle of Rosario
Strait, about 2 miles west by north of Burrows
Island Light; the southernmost and largest is 37
feet high. There is deep water close-to, and passage may be made on either side of the rocks.

Belle Rock, bare at extreme low water, is about
0.5 mile northeastward of Bird Rocks. A light is
on the rock.

—UNITED STATES COAST PILOT #7

June 28, 1978
Afternoon
Prince William Sound, Alaska

At Port Valdez, the summer sun poured down on the *Grand Canyon.* For three hours the huge blue and red oil tanker had been sitting at Pier 4 of the 800-acre Pipeline Service Company facility, filling her big belly with Prudhoe Bay crude.

The oil was hot—140° F. Pumped out of the lonely oilfields of northern Alaska, 800 miles away, it had flowed south through four-foot-wide weatherized pipe, across three mountain ranges, five major rivers and countless creeks and steams to the storage tanks of the newest oil port on the continent. Its ultimate destination: the gas tanks and home furnaces of California and the Northwest, hundreds of miles to the south.

She was still a new ship, just entering the second quarter of a tanker's twenty-year life span. Built in the early 70's in a shipyard in Maryland, at a cost of fifty million dollars, she had everything from air-conditioned crew quarters to main-engine remote control. Weighing slightly more than 120 thousand deadweight tons, 880 feet long, needing more than fifty feet of water to navigate in, carrying enough fuel oil to cruise for fifteen thousand miles—was it any wonder that Octogon Oil Company was proud to add her to its thirty-ship tanker fleet? Or that after the traditional bottle of champagne was broken against her curving bow, she was the star of the marine-engineering magazines?

For magazine covers she was photographed from the air and at an angle: bow to the front left, stern to the back right. Across her huge flat deck, large enough to hold three football fields, hundreds of meters of piping formed a gigantic blue cross. Through these pipes the hot oil ran, ran, ran, and ended up below deck in thirteen mammoth cargo tanks holding from three to six million gallons each. The *Grand Canyon* had a total liquid cargo capacity of 942,700 barrels: nearly forty million gallons. Had this cargo been transferred into one-quart cans (the kind that motorists buy when they change their own car oil) and the cans laid out side by side across the United States, the line would have reached from Seattle to New York, back to Seattle and back to New York again. Transportation of that much oil required a ship whose length exceeded by nearly 300 feet the height of Seattle's First National Bank Building.

The *Grand Canyon* was the same size as one of the world's most famous ex-tankers, the *Torrey Canyon*, which in 1967 ran into some rocks fifteen miles off the English coast. Before she was finally bombed into the sea by the Royal Air Force, oil from her punctured cargo tanks fouled scores of miles of French and English beaches. Thousands of seabirds died, prices for fish and shellfish tumbled and the tourist industry suffered through a key holiday period.

There was little concern that the *Grand Canyon*

would meet a similar fate. She carried "the latest safety, navigational, communications and anti-pollution equipment available," according to an Octogon press release at the time of the christening ceremony. To insure her safe passage through Puget Sound, the United States Coast Guard had established north-south traffic lanes, a vessel-traffic system and, most recently, shore-based radar. Members of the Puget Sound Pilots Association, who would guide the big tanker and her sister ships into the Sound from Port Angeles, were competent and experienced seamen with an impressive safety record.

Oil poured into the Grand Canyon from paired, cone-topped storage tanks on the hill above her berth. The fourteen mammoth storage tanks—250 feet in diameter, 62 feet high—each held 510 thousand barrels of oil which would flow by force of gravity into tankers ranging in size from 16 thousand to 250 thousand deadweight tons.

The tanks were built on bedrock and surrounded by dikes, for this part of Alaska was one of the most seismically active areas in the world. In 1964, one of the largest earthquakes in history demolished the original town of Valdez and was felt for hundreds of miles. Bottom uplifts ranging from four to thirty-two feet occurred under the waters of Prince William Sound. A tidal wave overwhelmed the ships in Port Valdez.

Quake precautions had raised the cost of the Pipeline Service Company facility to more than a quarter of a billion dollars, and the terminal was not yet finished. As the pipeline's capacity was stepped up from its present 600 thousand barrels of oil per day to two million barrels or more, additional storage tanks would be built.

[5]

More and more tankers would drink their fill at Port Valdez before they journeyed south.

June 29
12:15 A.M.

Her tanks topped off, steel loading arms disconnected, equipment checked, local pilot on board, tugboat assisting, the *Grand Canyon* went to sea. Following a one-way-only traffic lane, she would pass the light on Middle Rock and enter Valdez Arm. North of Busby Island, the local pilot would disembark, and her master would take her on from there.

In the pale darkness of the Alaskan summer night, the glacier-capped mountains rising high above Valdez watched the tanker go and were silent.

Twelve hundred miles to the south, a Coast Guard patrol boat received a report that a Russian trawler was fishing illegally off the entrance to Juan de Fuca Strait, and closed in to investigate the violation of the twelve-mile limit.

The fishing vessel, watchful and nearly full of fish, managed to cut loose its huge trawl net and speed away. The net drifted loosely in the cold ocean currents until it snagged on some floating logs. The net and the logs continued to drift in the dark summer night.

June 29
5:00 A.M.

Off Hinchinbrook Island the *Grand Canyon*'s chief engineer stood on deck and breathed in the freshness of the early summer morning. So golden again today. Off to starboard he could see Montague Island—fine razor-clamming there.

How he loved this coastline, irregular as the pieces of a jigsaw puzzle, blooming in steep-sided blue fjords and mountain-topped islands. The entire coast south to Washington moved him mightily. Night-flying over it, say from Anchorage to Seattle, he knew from the absence of lights that this was terrain not yet drowned by the flood of mankind.

The chief engineer was becoming more and more tired of the works of man. "By their fruits ye shall know them," he often thought. He felt sorry for the fishermen who had waged a hopeless battle against the oil terminal. Only last night, he had heard some of their talk in a Valdez bar.

He started down to the engine room. Soon the ship would be in the Gulf of Alaska. Nice that it was summer. He could do without the Gulf's winter weather, some of the worst on earth. Fierce storms of the North Pacific shaped themselves here before raging farther abroad. It would be nice to glimpse a sperm whale in the Gulf. This was their summering ground. The whaling fleets were after them, of course. Whales were still being made into shoe polish, car wax, and margarine.

As he went below, he found in his mind the beautiful lines from Genesis: "And God created great whales, and every living creature that moveth, which the waters brought forth abundantly."

June 30
Noon

Her wake rolling gently out behind, the *Grand*

Canyon continued south. Night had once come and gone, and would come and go again, before the ship was in the vicinity of its first port of call.

The tanker's American crew had settled into the customary routines. When not at work in the engine room, the wheelhouse, or the galley, the thirty-eight men on board slept in their private staterooms or watched television in one of the tanker's lounges. From time to time they saw another ship. Flocks of passing seabirds paced themselves to the tanker's sixteen-knot speed and then disappeared. No land would be visible till they were much further south.

As she breasted the long swells of the eastern Pacific, the *Grand Canyon* carried a small portion of the more than seven million tons of oil being transported at sea that day by ships around the world. By the year 2000 this figure might rise to more than thirteen million tons. Oil was the biggest item in the world's sea commerce.

July 1
5:30 P.M.

On the cliffs of Cape Flattery, visitors beginning the long Fourth of July weekend watched the *Grand Canyon* leave the open ocean and make her approach to Juan de Fuca Strait.

"What kind of ship is that?" someone wondered.

"Looks like a tanker," another replied. "Doesn't have all the masts that a container ship would have. Look how big she is."

They looked and then went back to watching the waters of the Pacific swish in and out of sculptured sea caves below the cliffs. Some admired the little lighthouse on Tatoosh Island.

The sky had been clear but now the clouds were moving in from the southwest. The weather for the long weekend would not be good.

7:10 P.M.

Near Sekiu, a vacationer eating clams beside his camperbus pointed out to his wife how these oil ships had grown since his service in the Navy in World War II.

The T-2, at seventeen thousand deadweight tons, was the modern tanker of those years, and for several years afterward it was the typical tanker on Puget Sound. It carried six million gallons of oil in its twenty-six separate compartments, but now these supers carried that much oil in just one of their centerline tanks. Pretty impressive.

"Is that one of those ships people are making a fuss about?" his wife asked.

"I suppose so," said her husband, "but with these new ships there's nothing to worry about. How about another beer?"

9:30 P.M.

The *Grand Canyon* slowed to seven knots as it made contact with the small pilot boat that came out to meet it at Port Angeles. Ediz Hook light flashed green and white while Captain Edward Brown, the Puget Sound pilot who would guide the ship to Octogon's oil refinery north of Bellingham, climbed the Jacob's ladder and came on board. Far below, he could see the pilot boat rocking in the water. Then it pulled away.

The tanker's third mate, young and smiling, greeted Brown at the railing and took his overnight bag. As they walked to the bridge, the mate told the captain his latest joke. Brown still had a smile on his square, tanned face as he entered the wheelhouse. He greeted the ship's master and handed him a Seattle newspaper, neatly folded into thirds.

"Not much news tonight," he said. "Anything I should know about?"

"Nope," said the master, "everything's okay. Here's the docking slip. We made about fourteen knots coming down the Strait. What time do you expect to take her in?"

"Somewhere between 2:00 and 3:00," Brown replied.

"Well, guess I'll go below and read what news there is. Weather seems to be worsening, but it probably won't rain until morning."

Brown exchanged greetings with the quartermaster. The two of them, along with the mate, would be together in the wheelhouse until midnight when the watch would change. Then he switched the ship's whistle from automatic to manual. If you left it on automatic, you were never quite sure when it would blast, and it could make you jump out of your skin.

That taken care of, Brown checked in with the Vessel Traffic System at Pier 90 in Seattle. He notified the Coast Guard of his departure, speed of advance, and estimated time of arrival at the refinery. He also called in the time that the *Grand Canyon* expected to reach the first of a large series of buoys which the Coast Guard had put in place six years before to mark north-south traffic lanes in Puget Sound.

Each of the black and white striped buoys had a name. The first on the route was Buoy Romeo. Then came Romeo Alpha, Romeo Bravo and Charlie.

Until you got to Bravo, a little way up Rosario Strait,

the traffic lanes were each a thousand yards wide with a 500-yard-wide separation zone between them. But Rosario Strait was too narrow for these widths, so on the way north to Charlie, you just kept to the right. Ships coming south were supposed to do the same. Rosario Strait was full of rocks and reefs and had a lot of fog in summer, but Brown didn't worry much about these things. He'd been up Rosario Strait too many times.

The Vessel System reported no traffic along the first part of the tanker's route. The ship would call in again when it reached Buoy Romeo.

Brown had visited Pier 90 on several occasions. In his mind's eye he saw the Coast Guardsman on duty get out a tiny red plastic ship to represent the *Grand Canyon*, and place it on the illuminated model of Puget Sound on which ship movements were charted. The model always made him think of a huge blue and yellow pinball machine. As he continued to call in, the Coast Guard would change the position of the little red replica and notify other ships in the system if the *Grand Canyon* were coming nearby. Had Brown been piloting a cargo vessel, he would have been a blue plastic ship. Black was for tugs and gray for military vessels. Red meant a tanker.

As he turned away from the radio, Brown visualized the ship's course: northeast, then north through the heart of the San Juan Islands. All through Rosario Strait, fishing boats would be out in force. Sometimes a tanker ran over their nets.

Through the long row of squarish windows that lined the front wall of the wheelhouse and looked down on the huge deck several stories below, he could see Dungeness Light to the southeast and the lights of Victoria to the north. He wondered what Sam and Grace were doing. They were friends who lived along the scenic drive on Victoria's Ross Bay. They were probably sticking close to home, avoiding the crowds of tourists who would be visiting for the holiday. He and Irene must get over to see them soon.

"You look especially chipper tonight," he said to the mate. "What are you planning for the weekend?"

The mate was driving down to Seattle with plans to take his girlfriend to dinner at the top of the Space Needle. The mate took all his girlfriends to the top of the Space Needle, and he had a new girlfriend every few months.

Brown's mind returned to Sam and Grace. They had done a lot of travelling since their retirement and were especially fond of France. He had visited them there when he was in Grenoble to take a special training program offered for pilots of supertankers. He had felt a bit silly at first piloting toy ships around a little lake, but the trip had been worthwhile. French cuisine. . . . He remembered a certain chicken eaten at a country inn.

10:10 P.M.

Walking up and down, sipping coffee, Brown kept checking the ship's position and adjusting its course. He turned to watch a tow boat exit from Haro Strait. The long tow lines were another nuisance to be watched for, like the fishing nets. The mate was talking to the quartermaster, at the wheel, about his girlfriend. He claimed she looked like Greta Garbo. Brown was sure that nobody could look like Greta Garbo. He could still see her face at the bow of the ship at the end of Queen

Christina. He'd seen that film about ten times, many years ago.

Speaking of the bows of ships, somebody should relieve the lookout. He probably could use a cup of coffee. Brown could see the white flashes of Buoy Romeo a short distance ahead. Time to call in. He flipped a switch. The message was the same: no traffic, check in again at Alpha.

10:32 P.M.

Lying on the bed in his quarters, the chief engineer was reading in the New Testament. He had never been able to figure out why, according to Matthew, Jesus had cursed the fig tree. It seemed a nasty piece of behavior. Now, in Luke, there was another fig tree. This one was to be given a second chance and manured, rather than cursed. That seemed more reasonable. Sighing, he turned out the light on the wall and joined the majority of the tanker's crew in sleep.

10:45 P.M.

Looking up into the starless night sky, the lookout saw the red and white lights of a helicopter heading toward the Naval Air Station on Whidbey Island. His job was to keep track of fishing boats and other small craft. They did not report in to the Vessel Traffic System and the radar observer might not pick them up.

Being something of a solitary, the lookout enjoyed these watches out at the front of the ship. The bow was so far from the stern, where the machinery, accommodations and navigating bridge all were located, that a man felt quite alone out here. But in the daylight, watching the wooded islands go by and keeping sharp watch for a killer whale in the sparkling blue waters, it was even nicer.

10:55 P.M.

On the San Juan Islands, thousands of people were asleep. They slept in the hotels of Friday Harbor and at the big white resort on Orcas Island; they slept in camperbuses and tents among the cedars at Moran State Park; they slept in summer homes and cabins on Lopez and Guemes and Decatur.

On the mainland, at Anacortes, families slept in their cars at the state ferry dock. The ferryboats were crowded and vacationers wanted to be sure to get on board next morning. They, too, were headed for the islands.

11:05 P.M.

At Romeo Alpha, the message was the same. No traffic, report in again at Bravo.

11:20 P.M.

A huge net from a Russian trawler, carried by the flooding tide, got caught, unseen by any observer, on the propeller at the stern of the *Grand Canyon*.

11:30 P.M.

"Say," said the mate. "I just heard about the near grounding off Clark Island last week."

"Yeah," said Brown. "That ship really was lucky. A complete power loss, and a tugboat just happened to be in the vicinity. They barely made it, though. The pilot told me himself it was a miracle the ship didn't go aground."

[14]

"Good thing it was a T-2," said the mate. "Can you imagine trying to stop this ship with one tugboat, if we had a power failure or loss of steerage?"

Brown checked in once more with Vessel Traffic. This time there was news.

The Coast Guard had been notified that the *North Star*, a fishing vessel in the tanker's path, was taking on water. A Coast Guard cutter had been sent to the scene from Anacortes. Fishing boats and a tug, the *Ocean Queen*, were standing by.

"Better put her over to the left," Brown said to the helmsman. "We don't want to get into that."

"Right."

They sailed for a few minutes in silence. Brown drained the bottom of his third cup of coffee. He wondered if his wife had remembered to call everyone for their Fourth of July barbeque on Tuesday. At night the grandchildren would want to see the fireworks over Elliott Bay.

A few more minutes went by.

"Put her back to the right," he instructed the quartermaster. The light on Belle Rock shone strongly off to starboard. It must be less than two miles away.

The ship did not seem to be turning.

"Did you hear me? You're still moving straight ahead."

"I heard you, Captain. I've got her over, but she's not answering."

"Well, put her hard right."

They waited, staring at the lighted dial on the rudder indicator.

"My God, Captain. She's not steering!"

Brown kept his eyes fixed on the indicator. There was

some mistake. Something must be wrong with the indicator. Surely the rudder was starting to respond.

He waited.

Somewhere in the room a voice kept asking what the
hell was going on.

The ship kept moving straight ahead.

Brown felt as if all the blood had been drained from
his body. He forced himself to speak.

"Use the public-address system," he said to the
wild-eyed mate. "Tell the lookout to get the anchor
down."

11:51 P.M.

In the middle of the chief engineer's dream, a bell
began to ring. Coming awake, he knew it was one of the
ship's alarm bells. What could be the matter? What time
was it? He fumbled for his watch.

Suddenly he was aware that the room pulsed with
an immense vibration. "Lord, what are we doing?"
thought the chief engineer. "It sounds like the engines
are on full astern!"

He was just reaching for his shoes and socks when he
heard a long grinding noise coming from the stomach of
the ship. His own stomach turned over. The noise went
on. Abruptly, he was knocked off his bed against a wall.

The tanker *Grand Canyon*, out of Port Valdez, was
aground on Bird Rocks.

2

July 2
3:55 A.M.

"Mr. Jensen? Coast Guard here. Sorry to wake you up, but there's a problem."

"Yeah?"

"There's a tanker aground on Bird Rocks up in Rosario Strait, and it's losing oil."

"Losing oil?"

"We don't know how much yet, but we think it's bad. At least one tank was ruptured."

"How long ago?"

"Just before midnight."

"Who else has been notified?"

"We've reached Fisheries. We haven't reached Game."

"What about Horn?"

"We've tried him several times, but there's no answer."

"What about O'Shea?"

"We tried him, too, Mr. Jensen, but couldn't get him. It looks like it's you."

Oran Jensen, third man down on the oil-spill totem pole of the Washington Department of Ecology, felt a stir of panic. "I'll get to Anacortes," he said. "Just as fast as I can."

5:30 *A.M.*

Russell Lindstrom, a Bellingham fisherman, went out to his garage to do some last-minute mending on his gillnet. He had missed the opening night of the sockeye season and he had a long day's work ahead of him to get ready for the second night. He turned the radio to his favorite country-music station and didn't hear the phone ring inside the house.

His son came out to get him. "It's George, Dad. He says there's been a big oil spill."

Russell went to the phone and listened while his friend George Petrovich, calling from the Anacortes harbor, told him of the oil smeared from one end of George's seine boat to the other and the smell of oil all the way to the end of Commercial Street. "Holy Mother of God, Russell, we've been had."

Russell, thinking with regret about his unfinished net, promised to go down and have a look. "I haven't heard anything on the radio," he said.

As Russell was going out the door, his son was on the phone telling Radio KLAM that there was "some kind of oil spill" in Rosario Strait. For his enterprise he was later rewarded with ten dollars for KLAM's News Tip of the Week; it was the first report any of the news media received about the grounding at Bird Rocks.

7:00 *A.M.*

Kay Libby turned the car radio on to catch the weather report. She and her friend Philip Ling, both University of Washington students, were in her blue Volkswagen on Interstate 90 north of Burlington, headed for Mount Baker. They planned to go hiking despite gray skies that promised rain at any minute.

Kay tuned in just in time to hear the end of a commercial for mobile homes. Then, in the announcer's authoritative tones: "A large oil spill has been reported just west of Anacortes in Rosario Strait, resulting from the grounding of a supertanker bound for Cherry Point. The Coast Guard has identified the vessel as the *Grand Canyon*, belonging to the Octogon Oil Company. At least one tank has been ruptured, but the amount of oil lost is not yet known. The accident apparently happened last night around midnight. Keep tuned to——"

Kay turned to look at Philip.

"Let's bag Mount Baker for today," he said.

Within minutes they were on the Anacortes Highway, the first of the volunteers who would later be coming in droves.

7:30 A.M.

Public Relations Director William Berry was an early riser. A blond, athletic man, he was outside pushing his hand mower around the lawn of his Edgmoor home in Bellingham when the telphone call came. It was his boss at the Octo Refinery, Jack Diehl.

"Bill, I want you to get down to Anacortes as fast as you can," he stated. "The *Grand Canyon* went on the rocks last night and there's already oil from Cypress Island to west of Whidbey. Get down there and set up an office so we can refer all the questions to you. The switchboard is jammed and we've got our hands full."

A few more details from Diehl; then Bill Berry too was on his way to Anacortes, caught in the magnetic field that had Bird Rocks at its center. At Bird Rocks themselves, the gray morning light revealed the *Grand Canyon* fetched up on the middle of three jagged outcroppings, surrounded by the clotting and ever widening product of her violent hemorrhage.

8:15 A.M.

At the Lummi Indian aquaculture project north of Bellingham on Lummi Bay, Ernie Penn paced up and down next to the oyster hatchery. The call from the Coast Guard that had alerted him to danger at 6:00 that morning had hinted that this might be a big spill. As soon as a plane could be located for him, he was going to make a surveillance flight over the Sound to see how close and how fast the oil was approaching.

The 750-acre pond where the Lummis grew coho salmon, rainbow trout and oysters was surrounded by a dike, and the gates that let the waters of Puget Sound in and out of the pond could be closed to keep out the oil. Several times in the past the Coast Guard had warned the Lummis of oil slicks floating in their vicinity, and the aquaculture project had managed to escape damage. What worried Penn was not so much the threat of direct contamination of the pond by oil. The problem was that the fish and shellfish needed a constant change of fresh, cool sea water and the nutrients it contained. If the gates had to be closed, and the water impounded in the pond became too warm, the fish would begin to die within a few days. The oysters were more resilient, but they would lose much of their market value if they could not obtain sufficient food. July was the height of the growing season, the time when the oysters would normally double their weight every two weeks. In stagnant water disease might also become a problem.

Penn, a member of the Lummi tribe, had worked for the aquaculture project ever since its beginnings in 1969, for the last two years as the director. Throughout the whole time he had kept an uneasy eye on his neighbors at Cherry Point: an aluminum plant, an oil refinery, then a second refinery. The effluents from heavy industry were enough to worry about, but supertankers tipped the balance too far. Penn had often testified at hearings that supertankers should be kept out of Puget Sound lest a massive spill wipe out the Sound's fisheries.

He went inside to check his tide table and chart again. He had an uneasy feeling that the time had come when his testimony at hearings was to be vividly proved right.

12:00 noon

Thomas Hatcher, a biology professor at Huxley College, was in his living room with the Sunday papers when his wife called him to the phone.

He was one of thirty biologists living at various places up and down the Sound who had contracted with the Washington Department of Ecology to respond on short notice in the event of an oil spill. The program involved was called REACT—Research Evaluation and Control Teams. Each scientist was to go out with a team of students immediately after a spill and, using a previously agreed-upon sampling procedure, make a count of dead organisms found on the beach, on the offshore bottom and floating in the tide.

Immediate reaction was essential. The greatest visible

sea life mortalities occurred within thirty-eight to seventy-two hours, and studies begun once the critical seventy-two-hour period had passed might well result in underestimation of the destruction. Sea creatures were generally soft-bodied and quick to rot.

This spill would be the first big test for REACT, which was organized in 1976 under new state financing. The Department of Ecology hoped that the collection, counting and analyzing of dead bodies would show evidence of ecological damage that would stand up in courts of law.

Hatcher, with a mixture of annoyance and apprehension, looked for his telephone list of team numbers. He wondered how many of the team members could be reached on a Sunday afternoon before the Fourth of July. How many, like him, had not yet heard the news? How bad was it going to be?

From the moment that the *Grand Canyon* smashed its nose into the jagged, iron-hard rocks in the middle of Rosario Strait, crude petroleum poured relentlessly from the punctured cargo tanks.

For the first three hours the oil floated stealthily in the darkness, until a trail six miles long extended as far south as McArthur Bank. Then, as the tide reversed from ebb to flood, the oil moved north and made its first landfall on the shores of Strawberry Island and at Strawberry Bay on Cypress Island.

A large breakaway plume entered Bellingham Channel and hit the west side of Guemes Island early Sunday morning, but drifted south again when the tide reversed. Another plume, sidling up the Guemes Channel, smeared the north shore of Fidalgo Island from

Shannon Point eastward, and was under the pilings of the Anacortes waterfront long before anyone but the local purse seiners were out of bed. A small streamer, only two yards wide, curled into the Capsante Marina, where it streaked the hulls of a few moored fishing vessels, including George Petrovich's seine boat.

The ebb tide that began at 8:15 A.M. carried the vanguard of the first big slick twelve miles to the south. As it went it coated the shores of James Island. When the ebb ended, the slick was hovering southwest of Watmough Head, off Lopez Island. Then, with the flood tide that began at 2:30 in the afternoon, oil went ashore at Watmough Head, went ashore at Cape Saint Mary, crept along the beach of Shoal Bight, slipped through Lopez Pass, began an aimless wandering in Lopez Sound, spread up the east shore of Decatur Island, entered Thatcher Pass, hit Willow Island and touched the southwest shore of Blakely Island. Smaller slicks floated toward East Sound on Orcas Island and would eventually be blown by the wind into Buck Bay.

The same flood tide sucked a new front of oil, fresh from the tanker, up into Bellingham Channel, where it plastered West Guemes again. This time the oil was carried north of Clark Point, and from there slicks wandered north toward Lummi Island and Bellingham Bay. Off Whidbey Island, oil that had ebbed earlier in the day flooded north into Deception Pass, blackened the beaches of the state park, and crept into Burrows Bay late in the afternoon. As the oil moved north in the bay, boat owners working with booms managed to stop the invader before it made its way into the marina at Flounder Bay.

Then came the final ebb tide of the day. As night

returned, a slick hovering between Sinclair and Vendovi islands slid off to the south, moved down the beaches on the east side of Guemes, split at Southeast Point, dawdled in the direction of Padilla Bay and rushed out of Guemes Channel, hitting as it went the whole south shore of Guemes Island.

In the first twenty-four hours after being set loose, the oil, riding with tides, currents and winds, spread out like a contagion far from its original source. Seattle's Monday-morning newspaper carried the headline, "75 Miles of San Juan Coastline Coated in Oil."

The headline was already out of date.

3

"Ladies and gentlemen, have a cup of coffee and make yourselves comfortable. I'm Bill Berry. I want to introduce Lambert Bibb, vice-president of Octo's Western Division, who will brief you on the situation as we know it so far. Mr. Diehl, the manager of our refinery at Cherry Point, can't be here right now as he is naturally very busy coordinating activities at the refinery, but we have his appraisal of the situation. Octo's communications center for the incident has been established in this office, and will be maintained until the cleanup is complete. We will definitely keep the press advised of all new developments. Please count on our full cooperation."

Berry handed around copies of a press release while Bibb, a tall, calm-looking individual, began his statement.

"At approximately midnight on July 1," he began, "the 120-thousand-ton tanker *Grand Canyon* went aground on Bird Rocks. The grounding resulted, as far as we know, from a sudden loss of steerage that rendered the ship uncontrollable. The cause of this steerage loss

[25]

is not known to us at the present time. Octogon deeply regrets that this accident should spoil the near-perfect record that oil transport on Puget Sound has had to date.

"As nearly as anyone knows at this point," Bibb continued, "the *Grand Canyon* was punctured in one of its forward port-wing tanks. Part of the contents have leaked out. A salvage crew and divers are out there now exploring the possibilities of offloading the oil that remains in the ruptured tank and towing the vessel off the rocks. A boom is in place around the ship and skimmers are at work. The two new Spick-n-Slick skimmer-boom rigs purchased just six months ago by Spotless Sound Incorporated are on their way from Bellingham. As you may know, these rigs cost more than half a million dollars each. We will also be utilizing our new super-coagulant, Oil Corral.

"We don't have an exact figure for the projected oil loss, but I suspect it will be in the neighborhood of twenty thousand barrels. This would be a fairly large spill, as I'm sure you all realize, and we plan to call upon all the resources in our cleanup capability. Fortunately, Puget Sound will benefit from the oil industry's experience with past oil spills."

Bibb had the air of a general unveiling his battle plan as Berry brought out a display board. The first page was an engineering diagram of the new Spick-n-Slick skimmer boom. "These rigs have a rapid-mobilization factor that cuts by an hour the time we usually expect for them to become operable once they reach the scene," he pointed out. "Their skimming capacity is three thousand gallons per minute, under ideal conditions. As you know, weather conditions are not perfect, but they could be worse."

Bibb flipped the diagram over and pointed to a detailed map of the San Juans on which Bird Rocks were marked with a large red **X**. A horseshoe-shaped area was marked off in black, its rounded head between Cypress and Blakely islands, with plumes extending south toward Deception Pass on one side and toward the southern tip of Lopez Island on the other.

Bibb's well-manicured hand quickly indicated several locations on Lopez, Fidalgo and Guemes. "As you can see, oil has touched shore at these spots due to unfavorable winds and tides. So we are stockpiling straw and sorbents in these areas to minimize the impact. I'm told there is a prevailing flow seaward in these near-surface waters, so we can expect any of the oil that we fail to recover to be carried down through Juan de Fuca Strait and flushed out into the open ocean. There the damage it can do will be greatly diluted, if not completely prevented."

The next diagram was the same map keyed to bird species. "If you will permit me to count our blessings," he observed, "I will point out that this is not the season for migratory birds to be in this area. As you know, a major spill during the fall migration or wintering-over might have had a significant impact on the waterfowl population of the entire West Coast. I wish I could say that there will be no mortality. I can't say that, but I can say that we will do everything we can to handle this problem as humanely as possible." He beamed. "I can announce, ladies and gentlemen, that Octo, immediately upon hearing of this incident, made a blank-check donation to the Seattle Wild Bird Clinic. The clinic will coordinate volunteers and direct all efforts to treat and clean any affected birds."

[27]

A hand went up in the back of the room. "Yes, I know you have questions. Please keep them for just a few minutes. I want to introduce our research team."

Bibb turned around and indicated a group of three men and a woman lined up in chairs behind him. They nodded competently as Bibb announced their names and described their lengthy credentials: two marine biologists, one biochemist, and a fisheries-resource expert. They had been flown in from Los Angeles and would go to work immediately to study the effects of the spilled oil on marine life.

Bibb turned away from his diagrams and, folding his hands, addressed his audience with a sober gaze. "We are indeed distressed," he stated, "that this unfortunate incident should have occurred in spite of all our precautions. And we don't intend to minimize its seriousness. But at the same time we hope that it can be seen in its proper perspective—the larger picture of the enormous economic benefit that Puget Sound derives from its position as an oil-refining center and its importance to our nation. Alaskan oil has provided jobs and income throughout this area, and has insured the capability of the United States to supply its own oil needs in a national emergency. I call your attention to recent remarks by the chairman of the Senate Interior Committee, Senator Davidson: 'In view of our continuing dependence for our daily energy needs on oil imports from unstable countries in other parts of the world, the growth of North Slope production offers an essential bulwark for national security.'

"Now, if there are any questions. . . . "

Claudia Fitzsimmons from the *Seattle Times* had her hand in the air first. "Mr. Bibb, you have not said what

Octo will do if this spill affects the commercial fishing season. I understand that the first big sockeye run got underway Saturday night."

"Salmon are a very important resource for this area," Bibb stated, "and we are concerned. But what we understand of the habits of salmon is that they sense the presence of oil and other pollutants and tend to go down quite deep to avoid them. Adult salmon are affected little by the presence of oil. I think we can say that the runs are in no immediate danger." Bibb turned quickly to the other side of the room.

"An hour ago," Westley Fleeson of the *Bellingham Herald* said, "I received a telephone call from someone saying that oil had come into Friday Harbor. That's all I got. Do you have any information on this?"

Bibb turned to Berry.

"I'd be surprised if much oil had made it to San Juan Island," Berry answered. "Especially as far up as Friday Harbor."

"Then there's no chance the slick will get to Victoria?" another reporter asked.

"No possibility of that," Bibb replied. "As I said, it is my understanding that the oil is already moving into the middle of Juan de Fuca Strait. It will pass Victoria, in small quantities, but several miles to the south. Our Canadian neighbors are safe. We can at least be grateful for that."

"What about Seattle?" Claudia asked. "Will it get that far south?"

"Or to Vancouver?" asked the reporter from the *Vancouver Sun*.

"No. None of the major population centers." Bibb pointed them out on his map. "Seattle, Vancouver, Bellingham, Everett, Port Townsend, Port Angeles—none of them has cause to worry."

A question came from the back of the room: "Isn't this the largest oil spill on Puget Sound to date?"

"Well——" Bibb hesitated. "It may be; twenty thousand barrels is a lot of oil. But the quantity is not the important question. What is important is our capacity to deal with the spill. And I can say to you with confidence that with our experience and our resources and the cooperation of everyone involved, there will be no lasting damage.

"I believe it's time we concluded this press conference. Octo's communications center will be available to you around the clock whenever you need additional facts on this spill. We anticipate that everything will be back to normal within a week. Thank you, ladies and gentlemen."

Two blocks away, in emergency headquarters set up by the Washington Department of Ecology, a scientist from the University of Washington wanted an official estimate of the spill's size; cleanup volunteers wanted directions; an outraged woman from Guemes Island wanted the head of whoever was responsible; the director of the Game Department wanted to talk to Oran Jensen; and Oran Jensen wanted to go home. He remained in charge, since Horn was still in California, and he had been up most of the night.

Calls were coming in from property owners from San Juan Island to Bayview State Park, reporting that they had sighted oil offshore and could they please have some protection. Jensen could do no more than log the requests and explain to the callers that the skimmers and booms stockpiled for oil spills had all been sent out the day before. He had this from SOPS, the cleanup contractor hired by Octogon.

Jensen's head ached as he tried to puzzle out how anyone could coordinate cleanup on so many different islands with dozens of little cove beaches, bluffs and narrow gravel strips, many with no access except by water. Cleanup was hard enough, he knew from past experience, if you had just one long beach to work on. This time equipment and crews would have to be ferried or flown to hundreds of separate places. Clark Point on Guemes Island, for instance, was covered with boulders of all sizes, and these boulders were now covered with Alaska crude.

Jensen could imagine no way to clean something like that. At Santa Barbara, he knew, they ended up just carting away occasional rocks that were coated in goo. Anything to make things look as good as possible. But you couldn't cart off the whole beach at Clark Point.

The phones kept ringing. Jensen picked one up, listened for a few minutes, made some noncommittal remarks, then turned to his Game Department man. "See this?" he said, pointing on his chart to an area of Mac-Kaye Harbor on south Lopez. "This used to be a clam farm. There was a sign on the beach saying that here was a new industry for Lopez Island. That was the people involved in the farm calling up. They said the whole beach where their littleneck clams were planted is smothered in oil ten inches deep. They want to know what I'm going to do about it. I should have told them to get a lawyer."

They were interrupted by a messenger from the Coast Guard, who brought the news that the Spick-n-Slick skimmer stationed north of Bird Rocks had broken down. The moving belt that picked the oil up from the water had gotten jammed with straw and other debris.

"Jesus Christ," Jensen exploded. "Why are they telling me? It's a problem for SOPS or Octogon, not me." Jensen was beginning to suspect that it didn't make much difference anyway; the oil had already pushed past the few booms that had been mustered in time. The skimmers were recovering some oil, but they were too little too late. Oil was all over the place before equipment could even be mobilized. With a night spill, this was virtually inevitable; but even without the problem of chasing oil in the dark, it had often been pointed out that organization for oil-spill cleanup bore little resemblance to the highly successful model of the local fire department. When there was an oil spill, you got complicated maneuvering between an oil company, a cleanup contractor, state and federal authorities and perhaps a few other parties. It sometimes wasted a lot of time.

The heavy rainfall of an hour before had moderated to a light drizzle. The Anacortes harbor looked like the site of a fishermen's convention, with upward of 200 men milling around, their boots thick with sludge. Their gillnet and seine boats, some coated with oil, were rafted at the docks. The beginning of the sockeye season would normally have been a time of frenetic activity for the Puget Sound fishermen, but the spill had idled them as effectively as a strike, and with the same kind of frustration, for they knew that out there under the oil thousands of salmon were swimming by uncaught, an unrecoverable loss. Nobody had any idea what to do except to stand around, trade rumors and estimate losses.

Inside the Harbor Restaurant, Russell Lindstrom and George Petrovich sat morosely drinking coffee at the counter under a large mural that portrayed Mount Baker hovering above the blue waters of Puget Sound with a ferryboat and a log tow crossing among not-very-accurately depicted islands. On the shore the artist had painted in a romantic oil refinery.

Russell read aloud from that day's story of the spill in the Bellingham newspaper, then put the paper down in disgust. "All it says about the fishermen," he snorted, "is that the runs will not be affected and the season will proceed as usual in about a week. God damn it, George, why don't you call up for the Seiners' Association and make a statement?"

Claudia Fitzsimmons, sitting to their right at the counter, introduced herself as a reporter for the *Times.* "How does it look to you?" she asked.

George looked at her as if he didn't understand the question.

Russell responded, "I'm going over to Octo and see if they want to buy my boat to ferry straw around. Somebody might as well get some use out of it."

"How long before you can start fishing again?"

"It's hard to say," Russell explained. "I think a week is optimistic. They're saying the spill amounts to twenty thousand barrels, but even if that's all—and I've never heard of an oil spill yet where the first estimates were right—that's a lot of oil."

"Christ," George said, "if you sat down and tried to invent something to float around in the water and gum up fishing nets, you couldn't do better than set loose a tank of crude. If you get oil on your net, you might as well throw it away."

"The net will give off an oily stink, see, every time you let it down in the water," Russell pointed out. "The fish have a fantastic sense of smell. They won't come near anything that smells like oil—not even a little bit. And nets aren't cheap."

"How much do they cost?" Claudia asked.

"My gillnets cost about thirty-five hundred dollars. George's seine nets are fifteen thousand dollars each."

"Who would buy the salmon anyway?" George asked. "Buy seafood from Puget Sound after our biggest oil spill? Who are we kidding? Do you know what happened in England after the *Torrey Canyon* spill? Nobody would buy fish, even imported fish!"

They ordered more coffee. George grew gloomier. "My son told me last year I should give up fishing. 'You're an antique,' he tells me. 'Not to mention dumb. Why don't you go to work for one of the local refineries and make twice as much as you do now?' he tells me. 'Face it, Puget Sound is for industry, not for fish.' 'I like to fish,' I tell him. 'I make all the money I need.' But maybe I should have listened."

"We're used to catastrophes hurting the runs and cutting into our season. Some of us used to fish the Columbia before the dams ruined it. But my God, if this gets the smolts, it could be the worst disaster for Fraser River salmon since Hell's Gate fell in."

"Where and what was Hell's Gate?" Claudia asked.

Russell explained that Hell's Gate was a canyon on the Fraser River. In 1913 and 1914, dynamiting there caused landslides that blocked the sockeyes and pinks in their migration to upriver spawning areas. The record runs of sockeye—as many as twenty-five million fish were caught in 1913—were wiped out. The catch went down to less than 20 per cent of what it had been. "In recent years the catch has been building back up with the help of spawning channels, hatcheries, fishways around dams and strict regulation. But what's the point if, when the fish move south from the Fraser through Puget Sound and out Juan de Fuca Strait to the Pacific, the young sockeyes and pinks are wiped out by oil? Of course you wouldn't notice it right away. The fish born in the Fraser wouldn't head back home to spawn the next generation until one to three years later. Then they might just not turn up."

"Salmon are fantastic fish," George added. "Nobody has figured out yet how they know to get back to the rivers they were born in. Some people think they have an olfactory nerve that can pick up the odor of the water down to one part per million. Now think about what oil could do to that. Okay, so the adults are picking their way along, looking for the river that smells right, and they run into the oil and that throws the whole system out of whack. Then they'll just mill around and die. They sure as hell will never get to spawn, and that's good-bye, salmon."

"George is right," Russell said. "Sure, we'll lose money this year by not being able to fish, and that's bad enough. But what scares the hell out of me is to think what this could do to our fisheries in the long run. You always hear about what a great economic boon the oil industry is to the Northwest. What about the fishing industry? The commercial and sport fishing in Puget Sound is worth more than $100 million to this area

[35]

every year. Why, up where I come from, Whatcom County, fishing is our largest industry. A Sea Grant study showed that there were more people employed in the fishing industry—catching and processing—in that one county alone than in all the state's oil refineries put together. Can we afford to lose that? Sure, we need oil, we all use it. But that doesn't mean it should be carried in those damn ships over one of the finest and cleanest estuaries in the world."

Claudia asked what the fishermen of Puget Sound had done to fight off the oil industry.

"Come on, Russell," George urged. "Tell her how the fishermen got together." Turning to Claudia, he said, "Russell's been trying to form a fishermen's lobby against tankers for ten years. And every once in a while, when the seiners aren't fighting the gillnetters, or the gillnetters aren't fighting the seiners, he gets the membership to pass a resolution or two."

Russell stared lugubriously into his cup. "Getting fishermen together is like getting the UN working," he explained. "Too God-damned many individualists. Too bad the oil companies don't have that problem. One big lobbyist in Olympia represents about ten of the major oil companies. It makes you wonder how much competition there can be in the industry if one man can represent them all.

"It's very hard to get any of our guys to worry about how to protect and build up the salmon as a resource. They don't see pollution as their biggest problem. There's always a more immediate enemy to bitch about: the Koreans, the Russians, the sportsmen. Try to talk to them about conservation! The fisherman's main method of conservation has been to put the other guy out of business."

George stirred himself to mild disagreement. "You can't say nothing has been done. We've given quite a bit of money to help keep some politicians in office. And the seiners were pretty strong behind the initiative to stop supertankers."

"George, that was maybe a dozen people like yourself who worked very hard. The others—they'll sign petitions, but they won't take them around. They'll sign letters, but not sit down and write them. They'll talk a lot—to people that already agree with them. They won't go to Olympia and beat on the doors of the legislators."

George did not respond immediately. Some fishermen he knew were hedging their bets when it came to fishing versus oil. Fishing was a fluctuating, sometimes seasonal, occupation threatened as much by foreign competition as by pollution. The growth of heavy industry seemed to hold out an assurance that there would be some other job when the last salmon had been sold. It was the old story of trading the ups and downs of small-scale enterprise for the stability of corporate employment.

To Claudia he said, "We're brainwashed. We've given and given for years and years. We've been pushed around by the logging companies and squeezed out by the hydroelectric-power people. Tankers are just more of the same. Big business. The fishermen have given up thinking anything can be done about it, and the oil industry keeps saying that it and the fishermen can 'peacefully co-exist' on Puget Sound."

"That's their line, isn't it, George?" Russell observed.

"Peaceful co-existence means do it my way and we'll all get along. And of course with the oil industry, it's not just a pollution problem as far as we're concerned; it's a fight over space, as well."

He turned to Claudia. "I'll give you an example. A few years back we fought against extending one of the refinery docks farther out into the water. Gillnetters have to have lots of room to drift, and that pier was just one more thing to get our nets caught on. The further it stuck out, the less room was left for our boats, and let me tell you, we get pretty crowded out there. That spot, close to Cherry Point, was one of the best in Rosario Strait for fishing. A little later the buoys were put in the Sound to mark traffic lanes for tankers, and they catch the nets of the gillnetters drifting down the middle of the Strait. And it's up to the fishing boats to stay out of the way of the tankers. I've come too close to being run over by a tanker in the fog."

"I'm going to fish until Puget Sound is paved over," George announced, "but I'm afraid it's going to be downhill all the way. There'll be more refineries, more petrochemical plants, more tankers. And more spills. I may have only twenty years left to fish, but when I'm lying on my deathbed I would like to know that the Sound is still there, and there's still salmon in it and other living things. I don't know how to explain it, I'm not much good with words, but God damn it, it's important."

He stood up suddenly, obviously embarrassed. "I'd better go find my crew. I'm going to tell them to go home and not call me for at least a week. I wonder what the canneries are going to do; they were all geared up for the run, too. Nice talking to you, Miss."

Claudia watched them pull on white caps and wander

[38]

out into the drizzle. The fishermen, she knew, were not the only group who stood to lose economically from this spill. The Puget Sound tourist trade, now amounting to $350 million annually, would also suffer. Recreational property values would plummet, and pleasure-boat sales decline. The total monetary worth of commercial and recreational interests dependent upon the clean waters of Puget Sound was difficult to calculate; Claudia had seen estimates ranging from $500 million to $8 billion. By whatever process of figuring, the value of a clean Puget Sound was clearly astronomical.

It was almost time for Claudia to phone in a story to the paper. First, however, she wanted to check out Octo's estimates of the amount of oil spilled, twenty thousand barrels, with the Department of Ecology.

She found Oran Jensen in his office talking with a reporter from Vancouver. Behind Jensen's desk, a large chart of Puget Sound was taped to the wall. Black marks indicated the location of floating slicks and of areas that had already been hit. There was black around all of Guemes Island; black along all the northern part of Fidalgo; black on parts of Cypress; black on Burrows Bay and the islands in the bay; black along all of south Lopez and south San Juan; black up San Juan Channel to Friday Harbor; smudges of black on Decatur, Blakely, Orcas. More black lines showed where slicks floated offshore in Lopez Sound, were drifting in Bellingham and Padilla bays, hung off the dike in Lummi Bay, sailed behind Deception Pass, stuck to Whidbey, had been blown in the direction of Boundary Bay.

"The oil is still on the move," Jensen said. "If this bad-weather wind holds overnight, Victoria is going to be hit tomorrow. This big slick here"—he pointed to the chart—"will cross Haro Strait on tonight's ebb tide, go up here on the flood"—he indicated Gordon Head on east Vancouver Island—"and pour down along here on the next ebb. With a southwest wind, Victoria will be plastered and re-plastered. If only the weather would improve. What we need are northerly winds to push the oil out into the Juan de Fuca Strait. Push, I mean, that one big slick. We've got miles and miles of coastline coated already."

"Mr. Jensen, a few hours ago the Octo people told us that Victoria was in no danger. Now you're saying that it is. What's happened?" Claudia asked.

"I don't know what they told you," Jensen replied. "I know how it looks to us."

"There's a cooperative oil-spill agreement between Washington State and British Columbia," pointed out the Vancouver reporter. "Will you be able to help Victoria?"

"Help Victoria?" Oran Jensen looked incredulous. "We've got all we can do to help ourselves."

A phone call interrupted them. "That was Ernie Penn from the Lummi aquaculture project," Jensen said when he hung up. "They've just decided to close the dike; the oil is getting too close."

"What's happening to the ship?" Claudia asked. "Has it stopped leaking?"

"I'm waiting for reports any minute, from divers and from our latest surveillance overflight. Our job now is to get her out of there. On that hard rock she's grounded on, tidal flows will grind her up more and more. But it's going to take a while. Oil has to be pumped out to lighten her, air may be pumped in to give her more buoyancy, divers will have to patch up some of her holes so she doesn't take in water on her way to drydock. That's all hard and dangerous physical work and will take quite a bit of time.''

"Where will she be towed for the repair work?"

"Into the Naval Shipyard at Bremerton. The commercial shipyards in Seattle can't take anything that big. I understand Governor Newman is in touch with our senators to get permission from the Navy to bring her in.''

"Do you know what caused the steerage loss?'

"There's a story going around that a big fishing net was found caught on the ship's propeller. I don't know whether that had anything to do with it or not. I can't see how it could.''

"Excuse me," he said as the phone jangled again.

Suddenly Claudia noticed that his face went visibly pale. He hung up the phone and sank slowly back into his chair.

"That was the report from the divers and the flight aircraft." He spoke in a strained voice. "Here's the latest news: parts of four separate tanks have spilled. Two hundred thousand barrels. More than eight million gallons of oil.''

4

Victoria, the City of Gardens, was in full flower for the summer season. Every day by 5:00 P.M. all hotels and motels in the vicinity were booked full. Hundreds of vacationers strolled up and down in front of the Empress Hotel and the Parliament Buildings, looking out at the placid Inner Harbor with its boats and ferries.

Saturday, July 1, was Dominion Day, the start of a long holiday weekend. In Victoria, it was also the first day of the annual Pacific International Yachting Association regatta, an event that brought to Victoria about 200 racing boats, Canadian and American, and was followed with great interest by the city's many boating enthusiasts. It was a weekend when almost everyone in Victoria was either on the road, on the water, or on the golf course. The first radio report on Sunday of a tanker aground in the San Juans, many miles away, alarmed most listeners less than the arrival of sullen rain clouds and the revised forecast predicting showers for the next two days.

Years later, residents of Victoria would talk about that Sunday and what they had been doing when they first heard of what would afterward be known as the "Siege of Victoria."

"We knew that there was an oil spill opposite Anacortes," Edith Courtney, desk clerk at the Empress, would recall. "My only thought was that we had a bus tour coming over on the Anacortes ferry, and I wondered if I would have to release those rooms."

"My wife and I were drinking tea in the refreshment room at the Provincial Museum when we heard somebody mention an oil spill," Charles Lewis would remember. "Our son had just gotten married in London and was flying to Seattle next day. He and his bride planned to sail to Victoria on the *Princess Marguerite*. It never crossed our minds that the *Marguerite's* cruise from Seattle would have to be cancelled. But with the Inner Harbor boomed, she couldn't come in, you see."

Harold Guthrie of the Ministry of Transport, one of the first Canadian officials notified of the spill that Sunday, would recall that he knew from the start that it might be serious. But his first reaction was to put it out of his mind until the reconnaisance pilots came back with a first-hand report. He did not relish the prospect of disturbing Cecil Cory, first in command of the Ministry of Transport, who he suspected was just teeing off at the Uplands Golf Club.

So it was with a certain effort of will that Victorians came to believe, on that Dominion Day weekend, that they were in for more than rain. By Sunday evening, the news media had alerted virtually all of the 200 thousand residents of lower Saanich Peninsula to the likelihood that a large oil slick, moving generally westward, might be pushed by the southwest wind right onto their shorelines.

Cecil Cory, when finally summoned from the golf course, found Harold Guthrie uneasily paging through the ten-inch-thick official oil-spill contingency plan. "Forget it, Harold," advised Cory. "It's not worth your time." He calmly pulled a five-page list of phone numbers from his top left desk drawer, and handed the first two pages to Guthrie. "Here, start with Clean Seas Canada, then start tracking down log booms." Cory glanced at the first message received from the United States Coast Guard. "Dateline 2 July at 1400 hours," he read. "The oil-spill situation appears uncertain. Weather could be decisive factor. Preliminary preparations advisable." Cory picked up his phone and rang up Oran Jensen in Anacortes. Three hours and twenty-eight phone calls later, he began to feel as if he might be ready.

One of his phone calls went to the yacht club, where a message was left for Mayor Cameron Alexander. The message reached the mayor, an avid racer, late Sunday evening as he was returning from the first leg of the regatta, which ran to Port Angeles and back.

The mayor called the Victoria City Council into emergency session at 8:00 A.M., barely mustering a quorum of the eight members, since several were still out of town. "I'm sure you've heard by now that the oil from the *Grand Canyon* is headed our way," he told them. "The outlook is not good." He shared with the aldermen the most recent reports he had received from Cory on the progress of the spill, including photographs of the beaches on Guemes Island where some deposits were ten inches thick.

"We are not in a position to deal with this ourselves, as I'm sure we all realize by now," Mayor Alexander stated, "and the Ministry of Transport has already taken charge. Cecil Cory is on-scene coordinator. He has requested that we call up all useful city equipment and the work force to operate it, and that we appeal to the citizens for help and cooperation."

"I hope the Ministry of Transport knows what it's doing this time," one of the aldermen said. He had uneasy memories of previous spills where decision-making errors had wasted precious time. At the *Vanlene* spill of 1972, it took three days to get a boom around the ship, and the peat moss was late in arriving.

Another alderman wanted to know if the city would be reimbursed for all its expenses. The mayor nodded. "Just before this meeting," he said, "I talked to Lambert Bibb, one of the senior Octogon officials, and secured from him a promise to pay for all cleanup costs that might be incurred."

The mood of the council was venomous.

"Cleanup costs? What about punitive damages?"

"I say ring up Ottawa and have them invoke the 200-mile limit at once. No more tankers off our coast!"

"If Ottawa had played its cards right in the first place, that pipeline needn't have been built and we wouldn't have tankers."

"Let's send the Air Force over there to firebomb that damned ship and sink it before it loses more oil!"

"Well, it's a deplorable thing," said the mayor, "and it couldn't have happened at a worse time, really. But we'll have to act quickly. I am told that we have one day, twenty-four hours at the most, to make our preparations. Recriminations will have to wait."

There were more rumblings, but the council soon voted to make available all of the municipality's highway trucks, mulchers and graders; to put the road crews and park-department personnel under Cecil Cory's direction; and to instruct the city's police to regulate beach access and shoreline traffic. A state of emergency was declared.

Mayor Alexander's appeal to the citizenry for help and cooperation was broadcast all day long. But it was not really necessary, for people were already turning out in large numbers; closing their stores; leaving their jobs; offering their private cars, trucks and boats; and turning up at the beaches with shovels, pitchforks, rakes and even brooms and mops.

Always conscious of their dependence on the sea, Victoria's inhabitants had been fearful of a calamitous oil spill for a long time. Surrounded on all sides but one by salt water, Victoria was as vulnerable as any city in the Northwest to marine pollution, and this vulnerability had a clear economic shape. The main industry, tourism, brought in more than fifty million dollars yearly for the city; among the leading attractions were a clean, pleasant harbor, two aquariums and numerous facilities for sport fishing and sailing. Five thousand local pleasure boats represented a marine investment of many millions of dollars. The 224 racing boats registered in the P.I.Y.A. regatta, now abruptly cut short, were worth an average of twenty thousand dollars each. The owners were trying to find guaranteed safe cover for their boats; Cameron Alexander had sent his son off with his sloop *Honoria* to find a berth in Seattle. More than 200 commercial salmon trollers who fished out of Victoria stood to be affected right at the peak of their fishing season.

It was, of course, much more than an economic stake in the outcome that brought the Victorians to the battlements. They loved the sea and were protective of the gulls, ducks and other birds and animals that shared their marine environment. (Cecil Cory's later report on the spill would estimate that so many people were concerned about the birds that for every oiled bird there were two volunteers, a fact, he noted, which in no way helped the birds. He and his staff tried diplomatically to redirect most of these volunteers to peat-moss brigades, leaving bird care to an experienced group from the ornithological society.)

That same Monday morning, while the city council was officially endorsing his efforts, Cory was meeting with the task force that had been set up under the contingency plan to assist him. In this group were two biologists who raised the question of what, if any, materials besides straw and peat moss were to be used in collecting or otherwise disposing of the oil. Using detergents to disperse it, of course, was out of the question; their killing effects on marine life had been realized after the Torrey Canyon spill of 1967, when it was found they did more damage than the oil itself. What Cory now proposed instead was to order large amounts of sinking agents: chalk and sand treated to make them oil-collecting.

The biologists objected. Sinking the oil, they pointed out, did not really get rid of it. Instead, sinking drove the oil down into the bottom sediments where it could never be recovered, and where its lethal effects, especially on shellfish, could be felt for years. The discussion went on for some time, but the biologists failed to convince Cory. His charge was to "clean up" the oil. If that meant sweeping it under the rug, so be it; his belief was that aesthetic pollution was first and foremost. Cory was a very competent administrator. He was willing to listen to the opinions of the task force, and add them up along with his own experience, but in the end the decision would be his. He had been to his share of public meetings and had come away with the distinct impression that most people would react more emotionally to the appearance of beaches than the health of clams. Though he was later to be the target of considerable criticism for using the sinking agents, he never apologized for it. "I would be criticized for any decision," he said.

Cory would look back on Monday, July 3, the day of the preparations, as being at once too long and too short. The logistics were complicated. His first objective was to deflect the oil away from Victoria and out toward the middle of Juan de Fuca Strait. It was obviously going to be impossible to protect the long coastline southwest of the city from Esquimalt Lagoon to Rocky Point, but perhaps the city itself could be spared. With the hope that the best defense would be a strong offense, he sent hundreds of feet of the strongest booms available out with the Navy as a frontal attack against the advancing slick. The booms were positioned just off Discovery Island, on Victoria's eastern flank, in a long barricade at a slight angle to the movement of the oil. Other booms were placed near these in **V** formation, with skimmers waiting in the apex of the **V** to lap up the oil as it was guided toward them.

Cory was a great believer in skimmers, though their effectiveness had been proven only in small, easily contained spills. Asked once by a reporter what he would do with a large spill, he had replied, "With a major spill all you need is more skimmers. And you need them quickly." His Sunday-night call to the senior pollution officer of the Ministry of Transport in Ottawa had requested, among other things, that at least ten, and more if possible, be sent out immediately by Hercules aircraft. These arrived with booms late Monday evening and were deployed in the coves and harbors around Victoria by crews working through the night with spotlights.

Cory relied greatly on the Navy for his seaborne defense. At the base just west of Victoria on peaceful Esquimalt Harbor, the news of the oil invasion arrived like a cannonball, galvanizing sixty-four-year-old Admiral McIntyre into a hitherto unsuspected force of energy. It was he who set in motion the ingenious scheme of installing snow blowers on the backs of destroyers, which would then go out to meet the oil and blow peat moss into it. It was also McIntyre who thought of sending the Mars bomber seaplane—a monster-size aircraft—to the Fraser Valley to pick up peat moss (a material favored over straw by Cory for its sorbent qualities). McIntyre experienced the activity of coping with the disaster almost as a solace. He dispatched Navy ships to assist in the placement of booms, he unrolled charts, looked up tidal currents, sent out a helicopter, and plotted the oil's advance with pins. He conferred with his counterparts in the Army and Coast Guard; they too were responding tremendously well with personnel and leadership. Though all their efforts would later be described as "a spit in the ocean" by an angry politician, still the Siege of Victoria was the finest hour for the military of Esquimalt Harbor. They were glad, at last, that they had something to do.

Besides the concentrated effort made by the authorities, there were also numerous individual defenses being prepared on that Monday. Every little cove and

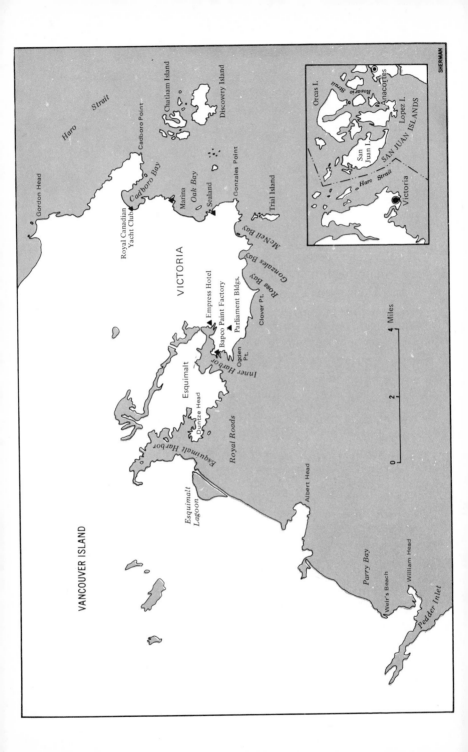

boat launch had its energetic battalion of property owners and beach lovers trying to figure out ways to make booms. Some fishermen stretched their nets across the mouths of inlets and intertwined them with evergreen boughs.

Meanwhile, a biological team from the University of Victoria had hastily assembled itself and was creating a quick, rough shoreline-sampling program to determine the variety and abundance of intertidal organisms at specific places along the shore. The team hoped to accumulate base-line data to judge the extent of the damage after the spill.

In downtown Victoria on Monday afternoon there were still many tourists strolling in front of the Empress Hotel. But with helicopters droning overhead, and convoys of trucks pulling up to unload booms and soldiers, the atmosphere was more that of a military staging zone than a resort. A Navy jeep patrolled nervously.

Through the warm and rainy Monday night, the population of Victoria worked and kept vigil. The ebb tide that began at 10:00 P.M. brought oil streaming across Haro Strait. Driven by the wind, it was impeded only momentarily by the wall of booms. At 5:00 A.M. Tuesday, just as the sky began to lighten, helicopter pilots monitoring the slick's progress watched it touch the eastern shores of Discovery and Chatham islands.

Then the tide turned and there was another respite while the oil surged back to the north and hung offshore parallel to Gordon Head and Cadboro Point. But at 11:30 that morning the tide turned again, and this time there was no respite. The invasion was on.

The oil came ashore in thin patches; it came in globs; it came in thick dark viscous streamers rolling in with the surf. It spread itself on the beaches and rocks below Gordon Head; it turned the corner and attacked Cadboro Bay and slipped with ease under the booms at the Royal Canadian Yacht Club, smearing the white hulls of the yachts. It played tricks: as it advanced into Oak Bay it left untouched the unprotected beach in front of Glenlyon Preparatory School and concentrated its foul-smelling advances upon the Oak Bay Marina. Here, a small island extended by boulders made a natural barrier, and the narrow south entrance to the harbor had been sealed off with more rocks. A semicircle of booms protected the north entrance, but only with marginal success.

Groups of people who had come out on the balconies of the Royal Alexandra and Dorchester and Rudyard Kipling apartment houses to watch looked on with horror as the oil seeped under the booms at the north end and, blocked by the rock plug at the south end from continuing its southward path, began to circulate all through the marina. The boats were coated in minutes.

There was a brief flurry of activity around Sealand, where a trained killer whale, penned in an underwater net, was hoisted out and placed in a truck for removal to a safer location. The rest of the animals were kept in their salt-water cages, supplied with water from an intake valve that reached twenty to thirty feet down from the surface. They appeared to be safe for the moment.

Meanwhile, the main branch of the slick crept on its leisurely way, hounded by helicopters overhead and prodded by the long booms that were being towed along next to it by a Navy vessel. The oil was diverted until it rounded the corner by the Victoria Golf Club; then the winds, still blowing from the southwest, pushed it toward shore with a force that rendered the booms practically useless.

The slick entered McNeill Bay, Gonzales Bay, Ross Bay; it touched Trial Island, with its little lighthouse. It plastered a beach that was paralleled by a sidewalk where hundreds of people stood by watching helplessly. A weathered sign posted here read, "Unsafe for Bathing—Water Polluted." Then on into the foreshores below Beacon Hill Park.

By 3:30 Tuesday afternoon the slick had reached the mouth of the Inner Harbor. Cory held his breath; this was the heart of Victoria, and defeat here would be extremely demoralizing. The oily surface of the water pushed under the first boom. Two slick-lickers working on either side of the harbor had some success picking the oil up at this point; repeated bombing with peat moss had turned it into a brown soup. Still it came on, advancing toward the Parliament Buildings.

The crowd gathered on the sidewalk in front of the Empress could smell the oil and could see the jumble of boats, planes and machinery that marked the advancing edge of the slick. The last set of booms crossed the harbor near Bapco Paint. The oily plumes crept up on it, lapped against the plastic skirting—and stopped.

Thwarted, the slick circled around and extended itself the length of the boom—but then the tide turned again and it began to retreat. Cory breathed a sigh of relief. Here, at least, the defenses had held. A cheer went up from the crowd as they saw the new backward drift and realized the Inner Harbor was going to be left alone.

That afternoon, in the long flood tide that lasted until 10:30 P.M., the oil retraced its path and coated again almost every rock and sandy beach it had hit in the morning and a few that had earlier been spared. Terse entries from the Ministry of Transport log for Tuesday summarized the situation.

Pedder Inlet: Oil coming in. Heavy pollution at Weir's Beach.

Esquimalt Harbor: Oil coating eastern harbor all the way up to the lumber mill. No work being done as more oil coming in.

Cadboro Bay: Heavy deposits on the beach at the head of the bay. Yacht Club marina about half clear. Cadboro Point very badly affected.

Oak Bay: New deposits on north side. No work being done as oil still coming in.

And so it went, into the night as the returning ebb tide brought yet a third coating to the harbors and beaches. Finally, the wind began to shift, the sky cleared and stars came out. Floating oil began to move out toward the Strait. When the residents woke up on the morning of Wednesday, July 8, the Siege of Victoria was more or less over. But Cecil Cory of the Ministry of Transport, flying over the blackened rim of coastline early that morning, had to accept the verdict that the oil had won.

5

July 5

"Good evening, and welcome to the six o'clock news. Today's lead story is the biggest oil spill in United States history. Governor Newman has asked the President to declare Puget Sound a disaster area; the state may ask the Federal Government to assume responsibility for cleanup operations; the Premier of British Columbia has threatened economic sanctions against the state of Washington; Prime Minister Andrews of Canada is meeting with his cabinet tonight to discuss courses of action Canada may want to take; and there are indications that the President may be coming to tour the oily mess that was once the San Juan Islands. More on these stories in a moment. Channel Four will have a special report on the spill at seven o'clock tonight."

"Good evening, this is Bill McGowan. Welcome to this special half-hour report on the effects of the big spill.

"We're here on Guemes Island with Professor Thomas Hatcher, biologist at Huxley College, Bellingham, leader of one of the state REACT teams. This beach is black thirty feet back from the water for as far as the eye can see. It stinks of crude oil and the putrefying corpses of sea creatures, and it's slippery as the devil to walk on. Since tides are lower in the summer, you can see how the oil didn't quite make it to those big drift logs farthest back by the bluff.

"Professor Hatcher, what is the spill doing to the marine life of the Sound?"

"That, Bill, is a very large question. Over all, I think it's fair to say that it's just as catastrophic as it looks. Eight million gallons is a lot of oil. This beach in particular has been totally wiped out. There are others that have been hit less hard, of course. But this is not like the small localized spills of the past. Prudhoe Bay crude is fairly thin and the spreading of this much oil at summer temperatures has affected a significant fraction of the surface of the Sound. It's especially unfortunate that it happened at night. Most mobile sea creatures are up at the surface feeding at night, and whether by immediate poisoning or by suffocation, the mortality rate has been very high."

"Will you be able to establish a firm body count, in order to put a dollar value on the damage?"

"We're trying. Let me show your viewers what we're doing here. This is the same procedure that we used yesterday. You see this length of cord running in a straight line from the high-tide line down to the edge of the water? Students are working along this line in pairs, turning over every rock in a meter-wide strip centered on the line. They're removing every dead creature they find and putting it in a bucket to be counted and analyzed later on. We do this in two or three places on the beach and this way we cover about one tenth of 1 per cent of the total beach area, a pretty good sampling. On this rocky type of beach it's not too difficult because most of the animals are on top of the gravel and pebbles. The sandy beaches are more work because they have to be dug up and sifted."

"What kind of things have died here?"

"Everything. Annihilation for all species. I've never seen anything as total, so much life all wiped out at once. Come up here to the high-tide line. These are the usual windrows of driftwood, foam and miscellaneous debris—now whipped up into a thick, gooey mixture with these small heaps of dead organisms. Your viewers can't experience the putrid odor that comes through even over the acrid smell of the oil. Many of these things are clams and crabs in the baby stages and other small crustaceans that you wouldn't ordinarily find on the beach because they'd be floating in the water. When they died they were washed in by the tide.

"If you've been on this type of beach before you know that what you'd expect to see when you turn over a large rock, as I'm doing now, is a mad scurry of eight or ten crabs running for cover. Look at this small black shell. This is all that's left now of *Hemigrapsus nudus*. You would normally see snails, periwinkles and limpets all over these rocks. They died immediately when they were hit.

"Or take a look at that irridescent puddle of oil several inches deep by that big boulder. That was a tidepool. The barnacles there are hardier than the limpets, but they couldn't stand up to this much stress. Some of them were alive yesterday, but today they're all dead. You know what anemones are—those soft little green animals that fold up when you touch them? All dead."

"Will they ever come back?"

"Eventually, I hope they will. It might be four or five years, though. After all, you have to have a breeding population. There are other areas—for instance, on the other side of this island—where the impact of the oil was not so great and some of the animals will survive. As the years go by, those will gradually repopulate the beaches left barren. But that will take time."

"What difference does it make, Dr. Hatcher, whether a few limpets and crabs on a few beaches live or die?"

"Nobody really knows what difference it makes, Bill. Because nobody knows very much about the role these creatures play in the total ecosystem of the Sound. I always think of the words of Aldo Leopold: 'The last word in ignorance is the man who says of an animal or plant, "What good is it?" ' There are still so many things we don't know about what goes on in these waters."

"Wasn't Puget Sound designated a special study area by a UN meeting in Rome in 1970?"

"Yes, because of its relatively clean condition compared to other bodies of water. It seems ironic, when you look around. Perhaps we're getting a glimpse of what it would be like if we were the only living species left on the planet. That seems to be the way things are going."

"Let me ask you about damage to plankton from this spill. Our viewers may know that plankton are the minute plant and animal creatures at the bottom of the ocean food chain. The food chain is like a pyramid of energy, with the plankton making up the greatest concentrations and numbers, then above them the small fish, then the larger fish, and so on. Plankton are the main source of food for shellfish too. What kind of damage have they suffered?"

"Millions of plankton exposed to oil were immediately killed. Of course plankton in the Sound are as numberless as the sands of the Sahara, but in areas where water circulation is poor, their destruction may lead to a localized lack of food for other organisms. In those areas, animals like clams, crabs and oysters may have trouble coming back because of this low food supply."

"What else is in trouble or dying?"

"Smelt, herring, juvenile salmonids . . . the bottom fish are being hit hard also: juvenile lingcod and halibut and flounder. They feed on or above the near-shore ocean bottom where large amounts of oil are frequently found. Adult bottom fish found in the same area will not be edible because they will be tainted with oil. Crabs are in the larval stage right now, so much of the crab nursery is wiped out."

"I've been taught that all life contains natural hydrocarbons. If that's true, why does oil, which also contains hydrocarbons, have such devastating effects on living things?"

"There are hydrocarbons and hydrocarbons, Bill. Those that occur naturally in living things I call biogenic hydrocarbons. However, there are other hydrocarbons and other organic compounds found in petroleum that are unlike any of the molecules usually found in biological systems. Modern techniques of chemical analysis can indicate the difference.

"Some of the non-natural molecules found in oil are soluble in water and can pass across biological membranes. Once in the system of a marine organism, they become destructive to it, like any poison. They may break down the membranes, or interfere with enzymatic reactions or possibly cause the formation of cancerous

[59]

lesions. These effects are associated with organisms found in oil-polluted areas.

"The presence of oil can, of course, do damage short of an outright kill. We've seen some pretty weird behavior in the last day or two. Bottom fish swimming at the surface, acting like they're drunk, paying no attention when a boat comes near. Their defensive reactions are shot. Even in small doses, oil may mask scents which sea animals depend on for finding food, mating or avoiding predators. It can stunt their growth or disturb their reproductive cycles. These low-level effects don't have the dramatic impact of the massive destruction you see on this beach today, but they are very serious."

"I'm afraid we're beginning to run out of time, Dr. Hatcher. I wonder if we could shift our emphasis here slightly. Would you say a word or two about what's happened in the light of world food shortages? Coastal waters like those of Puget Sound are the most important we have for fish and shellfish production, aren't they?"

"Yes, Bill. Nearly a fifth of the world's animal protein comes from the world's oceans, and estuaries like Puget Sound are the most productive ocean waters. The middle of the Pacific is, by comparison, a biological desert.

"Unfortunately our coastal regions are also those that are receiving the heaviest pollution—not just oil pollution, of course, but pollution of all kinds. Our fish-breeding and shellfish-breeding nursery areas are more threatened each year by all forms of coastal and industrial development. This is at the same time that world populations continue to expand and entomologists hold their breath as they watch whole continents being planted in one or two strains of high-yield wheat or rice, monocultures which are greatly vulnerable to disease. I personally feel that we have a moral obligation to preserve our productive coastal regions from further degradation.

"Of course the problem is complicated because the world economic system is much more of a stumbling block than pollution is when it comes to feeding that large part of the world's population that goes to bed hungry every night and gets up hungry every morning. Back in 1967, the President's Advisory Committee on the World Food Supply estimated that as many as a billion and a half people in the world were receiving too few calories or too little protein. Yet the anchovy catch from the coast of Peru was going into American livestock feed. We feed twenty-one pounds of fishmeal or high-protein grain to one of our cows to get back one pound of steak—wasting twenty pounds of protein in a protein-starved world.

"I wonder if we can ever get more young people in this country to focus their attention on world trade patterns, foreign aid and world economic development. The increasing emphasis on domestic concerns that began with our withdrawal from Southeast Asia shouldn't be allowed to blind us to problems of world poverty."

"Thank you, Dr. Hatcher. I'm afraid our time is up. Thanks to our viewers for being with us.

"This is Bill McGowan for Channel Four."

"This is Malcolm White. I'm standing here beside the 750-acre pond where the Lummi Indians have, for seven years, been raising salmon, trout and oysters.

"This is a beautiful place; Mount Baker looks down

on the waters of the pond, and great blue herons wing their way overhead. Normally, small silvery fish would be constantly popping up out of the surface of the water, as if to show that they too enjoy the setting.

"But they aren't jumping today. The fish in this pond are dying, fouling the stagnant water as they turn belly up, hastening the death of their fellows who are still alive. By the end of the day tomorrow the Lummis expect to be the owners of five million bloated dead fish.

"This reporter hardly has the heart to ask the Lummis how they feel about what has occurred. I was here in June, 1971 when the tribe celebrated the completion of the three-mile-long, twelve-foot-high dike that members of the tribe had built by hard physical labor on the tidal mudflats of Lummi Bay. Scores of tons of rock, sand and gravel had been carted and bulldozed into place to make the semicircular dike. On that last day the final bit of work had to be completed before the tide went out. Then water would be impounded behind the dike and the tribe would be in business. It was a critical moment. Two bulldozers, one working from each side, raced to close the final gap—and succeeded.

"The jubilant Lummis celebrated with a salmon barbecue and tribal songs and dances. It looked as if the dream that the tribe had been working to make real would indeed come true. It was a dream of self-sufficiency and renewed tribal pride, of getting off welfare and away from poverty, of finding a cash base that would support the sixteen hundred persons on the tribal roll and would also allow the Lummis to preserve what was left of their tribal lands and waters. Before the idea of aquaculture was brought to the tribe by a young professor of biology from Western Washington State

College, the Lummis had thought they had no choice but to lease their tidelands to the white man for industrial development.

"In 1969, research ponds were built for an aquaculture feasibility study. The Lummis worked to dike these smaller ponds during the winter and at night: up to twelve hours a night, seven nights a week, and in three months they had moved seventy-five thousand cubic yards of sand and rock. The research projects indicated that a major aquaculture project was indeed feasible. Government agencies that had funded the initial experiment were joined by others in providing assistance to the tribe, and the Lummis established their own manpower-training program to develop a skilled labor pool. Tribal members went to college to learn business-management techniques.

"Slowly, a new feeling of pride and confidence developed. One tribal member told me when I came here to cover the big dike celebration, 'We're walking a lot taller than we did two short years ago.' Another said, 'I feel if we can do this we can do anything.'

"He spoke of the many additional dreams that depended on the success of the big project. Its financial earnings would make possible better tribal housing, health care and education. These in turn would enable the children of the tribe to share in the opportunities available to more prosperous people of the white society. But older men, too, had dreams for themselves, of new kinds of businesses that they would start on the side, because a people who could imprison the tide could do anything.

"But there were problems: water temperature, siltation, engineering failures. Critics attacked the project because its costs were greater than had been anticipated. Slowly the years passed. There was the year of the first big harvest, the year of the first small profit, the year when the national media arrived to document the Lummi success story. But through it all the Lummis were always aware that a spill from a tanker accident could wipe out all the work, all the confidence and all the dreams.

"I've asked some of the Lummis what they will do now. Most of them just shrug and look away. The sun is setting here at the Lummi project in more ways than one. I hope that somehow it can rise again.

"This is Malcolm White for Channel Five."

"Good evening, this is Governor Newman. I am speaking to you tonight because I share with all of you, the citizens of Washington and our friends throughout the nation, the deepest sorrow over the events of the past few days.

"This morning I accompanied Prime Minister Andrews of Canada on an aerial tour of Victoria and the San Juan Islands. He was appalled, as I was, at the spectacle of our beautiful coastlines coated for miles in oily sludge, at the total disruption of a way of life that too many of us had come to take for granted.

"Puget Sound country deserves better. We cannot undo the damage that has been done, but we can and we must keep looking to the future. I am therefore calling the state legislature into special session beginning two weeks from today. The sole business before the session will be the devising of an oil policy for this state to insure that—whether it be a year from now, five years from now or twenty years from now—never will we go through this again.

"In the meantime, I have asked the oil companies to voluntarily suspend supertanker operations on our state's waters.

"In the many thousands of messages which have poured into this office, you, the people of Washington, have made your feelings clear. I hope that you will continue to direct letters and telegrams to your state representatives. Government will work if you make it work.

"Thank you, and good night."

"Good evening, and welcome to the eleven o'clock news. Octogon Oil Company tonight refused to suspend supertanker operations on Puget Sound, calling the governor's request for a voluntary suspension a 'sincere but misguided appeal.' Halting all supertanker operations on Puget Sound because of one oil spill, Octo spokesmen said, would be like shutting down the entire state university system because of a riot on one campus.

" 'The people of this region need oil products,' Lambert Bibb, an Octo vice-president, has said. 'We intend to see that their needs are met. Those who are labelling recent events a disaster should keep in mind that not a single human life has been lost.'

"Bibb's statement continued, 'We can understand the governor's reaction in light of the intense political pressure being brought to bear on him by organized special-interest groups. But we have to compare this negative response to the positive dedication and good will of hundreds of cleanup volunteers working side by side on

Puget Sound beaches. Employing the very latest technology and materials supplied by Octo, they have shown the determination to get the job done. And, with expert direction and leadership, the job is getting done!' "

6

Kay Libby, twenty years old, wasn't sure why, but she had a strong feeling that the Grand Canyon spill would be a checkpoint in her own life, something she would have to remember. For the first time since she was thirteen she began to keep a diary.

July 6
South Beach

After three days of working at Anacortes, Philip and I volunteered for cleanup work here on San Juan Island. By yesterday afternoon there must have been 400 volunteers checked in with the Coast Guard, but nobody seemed to know what to do with us. We've been working haphazardly just trying to sop up the oil with straw as it comes in. This morning Orlo Bixby took charge—he's the county civil-defense coordinator—and now things seem to be a little more organized. He's getting hot-food wagons and sanitation stations set up, and has started mobilizing us into teams to work on specific sections of beach. Helicopters are dropping bales of straw every few hours. First-aid units have arrived.

Already there have been injuries, people slipping on the rocks. We heard of a man who struggled for hours to boom off his own beach at the south end of Lopez, was overcome by fumes and had to be airlifted to Anacortes for treatment. Mr. Bixby has been warning all of us against overexposure and exhaustion. He admits that his agency was more prepared for nuclear attack or insurrection than for an oil spill. "This is not exactly our line," he said, "but we're doing a pretty good job keeping things moving."

Friday Harbor had been calling the Department of Ecology for help and cleanup personnel, so yesterday we ferried over from Anacortes on the *Klickitat*. Two hundred troops from Fort Lewis and great piles of straw on board. When the fog burned off, it was a beautiful summer day. Coming through Thatcher Pass, we passed dozens of blackened beach strips, beaches I remember from sailing around here last summer. It's an eerie feeling, like walking through familiar forests after they've been clearcut.

The ferry went right through several large oil slicks in Rosario Strait, and we could just make out the *Grand Canyon* and Bird Rocks to the south. Passed several skimmer boats at work. Helicopters were clattering around overhead on surveillance flights. I've never seen so many helicopters. Maybe it gives all the state and federal agencies now involved something to do. At least they look busy.

A few of the troops got off at Lopez, and we went on to San Juan Island. Coming into Friday Harbor we could see oil all along the coast and ringing Friday Island. Along the waterfront, oil coated the pilings of docks, the hulls of moored fishing and pleasure boats and the supports of the little gift shop on the water.

We were supposed to be met by a convoy of cars and

trucks to take us to the beach, but there was some sort of foul-up, naturally. Finally the postmaster got the idea of ringing the town fire bell. That got everybody together, and the mayor took charge. An hour later we were on our way to South Beach with pitchforks and rakes donated by the hardware stores in town and, I guess, by every farmer on the island. That was what the grand technology of oil-spill cleanup came to in the end: some farmers on San Juan Island handing out their pitchforks.

I've been to South Beach before. On an ordinary day, it has to be one of the finest beaches in the San Juan Islands, superb views of the Olympics across miles of sparkling blue water. And public, as too many beaches on the islands are not. What the narrow dusty road took us to yesterday was once a beach; I don't like to call it that now. I climbed out of the truck and walked up to the water just in time to see a greasy and flopping grebe, red eyes glowing like fierce coals, struggle into the water and sink. Dead birds that had been picked up along the shingle lay in a large pile, shiny, shapeless blobs. People would look at the pile and quickly look away. Far down the strand, somebody was burning soggy piles of oil-soaked straw. A black, smelly plume of smoke rose fifty feet into the air.

Rest of the day a blur of work, spreading straw on the oozy carpet of black that covered the gravelly sand in a twenty-five-foot strip, raking it up, carting it to bonfires. The smell of the oil made some people sick; a few even vomited. I got only a faint headache plus exhaustion and increased bitterness of spirit. Fortunately the local people are looking after us, bringing us food and water and offering shelter for the night.

July 7

More work at South Beach. The beach has been washed by the oily tides three separate times, and oil has penetrated the pebbles and sand to a depth of three feet. There is talk of plowing or bulldozing the whole contaminated surface, but what would that do to the fauna and soil stability?

We've been put up by a local fishing family. The wife is worried that the island's small cannery may not open this year. Her husband has talked with a graduate student who says that all kinds of specimen tanks and experiments at the Friday Harbor Marine Station have been polluted by oil coming into the water-intake pipes that carry water from the harbor to the marine laboratories. I wonder if the Shannon Point Marine Station and others have also been affected. I may hear tomorrow when Philip and I go over to work at Deception Pass.

Warnings are coming out about shellfish. The public-health authorities are spreading the word that even though a clam or oyster doesn't smell or taste of oil, it could still be polluted. I can't imagine that anyone would feel like eating shellfish around here right now.

The spill has somehow turned this into another world, with its own reality. No one talks about anything else. Somewhere, I suppose, there are beaches where the water is blue, the sand clean and the smell fresh and bracing, but I find that difficult to imagine.

July 8

We took the boat back, got to Deception Pass but couldn't work for several hours because the straw had run out. A Parks Department crew was busy with chain saws cutting up the driftwood and burning it in huge bonfires. The heat from the sun and the fires and the incessant buzz of the saws made it seem like a scene from Hades. A biologist from the State Game Department told us that three dead killer whales were found this morning on the beach near the Shaw Island ferry landing. They were all heavily coated with crude. Autopsies will be performed. A colony of harbor seals living on some rocks off Victoria is known to have been badly affected by the oil. The biologist said that the effect of a spill this big on marine mammals in the Sound will be severe. Harbor seals and river otters lose their body-heat insulation when oiled, and soon die of exposure.

Senator Davidson flew over the San Juans today with a party of other senators from coastal states. We heard him on the radio afterward. America, he said, must come down off its hydrocarbon high. Fifteen thousand dead birds might have clapped their wings in applause, but were unable to. The souls of dead killer whales must be wondering what Senator Davidson intends to do to implement this rich and novel insight.

The state park here at Deception Pass is a confused mess of gawking tourists, traffic jams, and would-be cleanup workers. The police are around, but they're just trying to keep traffic moving; there's no attempt to keep people out of the way. I'm glad about that—I think everyone should have a chance to see this for themselves. We finally started working again when the straw arrived. This is such a popular beach that the Department of Ecology has given it top priority for cleanup, but at this rate it's going to take all summer.

July 9
Deception Pass

Worked most of the afternoon at Bowman Bay. Still an unbelievable mess. Word has it that the beaches are all like this, from Victoria across the southern San Juans and even up to Bellingham. Weird ideas for coping with the catastrophe are being phoned in to the Coast Guard. One man suggested setting the oily beaches on fire and throwing on tons of fireworks to make a display that will attract the tourists back. Somebody else proposed setting off underwater demolitions to divert the salmon runs from Rosario Strait to Haro Strait. This morning I talked to a camper who had just been out on the ocean coast. A rumor was spreading like wildfire out there that a huge oil slick had been sighted moving toward the beaches of Olympic National Park. When the Coast Guard investigated, they found not oil but jellyfish—a floating mass of millions of small blue-black jellyfish known as *vellela*.

Saw somebody's beautiful Irish setter running up and down the beach, confused, bothered by the strange smells, maybe, and splotched with black goo. I'm getting pretty well splotched with goo myself. We don't even try to get clean at night. At least we've been eating well, thanks to the efforts of one of the local Granges. At noon today several women came down with big buckets of fried chicken, potato salad and baked beans. We put down our rakes, sat down on the beach and ate like hoboes. We're a motley crew. Besides us and other college students, there are a couple of housewives, a family from California that was taking a trip to the Cascades when this happened, a retired banker, two striking longshoremen, an English professor from the U.W. who belongs to the Audubon Society and a whole bunch of people from a natural-food store in Seattle. This is another one of those experiences where you say afterward, "Well, the work wasn't that great, but you got to meet a lot of interesting people."

Late in the afternoon, Philip and I drove up to Anacortes. We went out past the ferry dock to Washington Park where we could get another look at the *Grand Canyon*. We stopped at Sunset Beach and watched some workmen sent out by Octo trying to steam clean some oil-covered boulders that looked like cupcakes with run-away chocolate frosting. They had a hose with a metal rod at the end, and hot water pouring out. The boulder was fairly small, about two feet in diameter, but it must have taken them twenty minutes just to clean the front face of it. At twenty minutes a rock, how many centuries will all this require? Hopefully, the weathering process and the continual flux of the tides will scrub the rocks off as time goes on, but it's going to be slow.

We went off toward Fidalgo Head on the dusty, one-way loop drive that winds its way through Washington Park. It was bumper to bumper with cars and people like us, seeking a glimpse of the tanker. There it was, like a beached and wounded whale, listing gently to port, three quarters of a mile away across the blue waters of Rosario Strait. At that distance it was hard to believe that this was the instrument of so much destruction. There was a lot of hullabaloo around it, with helicopters overhead and small ships all around like scavengers. With Philip's binoculars I thought I could make out the yard-oiler that the Navy sent up from San Diego to take on some of the offloaded oil. The plan is to lighten the ship enough to get it off the rocks and then tow it to Bremerton for repair. I would have thought they'd try to get all the oil out before they risk moving it, but apparently they're afraid it will break up completely on the rocks. It's amazing how fragile that giant really is. The biologist on the beach yesterday told us that a tanker's strength is similar to that of a glass tube: it can withstand a lot of stress until the first crack or gash is made, then it goes to pieces quite easily.

I took a good look at Bird Rocks through the binoculars—three grayish, weathered domes, the highest one to the south. I feel a special connection to those rocks. One day last summer when I was out sailing we were near Bird Rocks and saw that each one had a sign on it. We went up close to read them and found they were markers proclaiming each rock to be a National Wildlife Refuge. Another thing we saw that we couldn't explain at first were numerous rusty metal cylinders, all over the rocks. Then somebody figured out that they were old shell casings from the early 50's when the Navy used Bird Rocks as a bombing target. Things have been fairly quiet at Bird Rocks since then, at least up to eight days ago. Gulls and cormorants inhabit the rocks, and at this time of year they are covered with seagull eggs and baby birds, fluffy little brown chicks with black speckles hiding underneath the rocks and crevices. Then the tanker came crashing in on them in the night—couldn't read the signs, I guess.

Around Anacortes I swear there are more news-media people than there are cleanup workers. I walked up to the Coast Guard office and was interviewed twice before I could even get in the door. The eyes of the world are upon us. This will probably be the best-recorded and most-photographed spill in United States history, as well as the biggest.

July 10

We took the day off from cleanup to come back to Seattle and rest. Feels so good to get into clean clothes! On the way we passed smelly trucks on Interstate 5 carrying dirty straw. Where are they dumping it? Disposing of all that oily straw is going to be a real problem. We also passed caravans of army trucks from Fort Lewis heading north.

When we got into Seattle there was a big banner over one of the freeway overpasses: "Visit Puget Sound, the Local Dead Sea. A Project of Your State and Federal Governments."

How wonderful it is not to smell oil for a while; only now do I really appreciate the contrast.

The TV stations are flashing the locations of bird-rescue stations and cleanup coordinating centers during their station breaks, and devoting most news coverage to the spill. Premier Barkley of British Columbia was on TV tonight expressing outrage that our state government had never devoted five minutes or five cents to studying the alternatives to sending large supertankers through the San Juan Islands. "We do things differently here," he said. "We don't let big business run the whole damn show."

As after Santa Barbara, the dispute over the amount of oil that has actually been spilled continues. Oran Jensen, a Department of Ecology official, was quoted as making an estimate of 200 thousand barrels, or about forty times as much as spilled in Anacortes in 1971. Then one of Octo's mouthpieces was on the news, claiming the spill was "only" 100 thousand barrels. It's a stupid dispute, ridiculous. When you're on those beaches, you couldn't care less whether it's 200 thousand barrels or 200 thousand pints. It's oil, and it's everywhere and it's still coming in.

The news showed the mayor of Victoria expressing regret at the burning to the ground of an Octo service station by some students from the University of Victoria. "I am convinced that the students did not mean to go so far," the mayor said. "It was one of those situations that get out of hand." Then there were shots of cleanup equipment that had been flown in from England being unloaded at Sea-Tac. The governor's sons at work with rakes and buckets on a beach. Pictures of Captain Brown, the Puget Sound pilot who was in charge when the tanker crashed, and the chief engineer, as they walked into Coast Guard headquarters downtown. They, and the rest of the crew, have been almost completely shielded from the press. They can't make any public comments until the official investigation by the Coast Guard is completed. Two very sober-looking gentlemen. They're probably worried that the blame will be fixed on them.

After the news there was a half-hour special interview with a marine architect who said that the *Grand Canyon*'s grounding appeared to have been caused by a problem with the ship's rudder. Said we would find out details after the inquiry. He was asked how often tankers have accidents. In 1969 and 1970, there were at least 338 collisions and 366 groundings of tankers throughout the world: almost one grounding or one collision each day. Of the total incidents reported, at least 151 resulted in pollution of varying magnitudes.

Groundings, he said, occur in all coastal waters regardless of ship-traffic density. He said that supertankers are so big that their crews sometimes use bikes or motorcycles to get around on deck; other ships have run into the big ones because the tankers' bow and stern lights were so far apart they were thought to be on two different vessels.

July 11

Controversy is building up about the new chamber of commerce ad campaign to keep the tourists coming here. The chamber is obviously worried that the national publicity on the spill will do severe damage to the tourist industry as happened in Santa Barbara after the blowout there.

The ads say, "Come to Puget Sound Country" and show beautiful color pictures of mountain lakes, Mount Rainier and unspoiled ocean beaches. Then there's a photograph of the Space Needle and elegant dining and dancing in Seattle, "The Capital of Puget Sound Country." The rumor is that Octo is putting up at least half the money for the campaign. They want everyone to know that nothing terrible has happened. Too bad they won't finish the message: "Come to Puget Sound Country, but Don't Look at Puget Sound."

The contamination of so many Puget Sound beaches has put terrific pressure on the ocean beaches. Many tourists who were already here when the spill occurred moved out of the spill areas. An oil spill was not what they had in mind when they planned their vacations. Some fled the San Juans and others changed their plans at the last minute. With all those people going to the coast, there aren't nearly enough campsites to hold them. Fistfights are supposed to have broken out at Kalaloch and Mora among tired, frustrated campers with no place to go. There just isn't any place to put all the people who already have "Come to Puget Sound Country."

Depressing as it is to be out on the beaches raking up oily seaweed, I find myself looking forward to going back as a pleasant contrast to being in the city. So many people here seem to be trying to pretend it didn't happen, or that it wasn't serious or that it has no significance for them, so they can get on with business as usual. I talked to Dad on the phone this morning. "They seem to have it under control," he told me. He was upset about the group of eco-guerillas who poured buckets of oil from the beaches all over Octo's office downtown. What they did was more shocking to him than the spill itself. I tried to tell a friend what it was like at South Beach, and how angry I felt. "What did you expect?" he said. "Why be shocked? Something like this was bound to happen, and this probably won't be the last time, either." I feel deadened by this world-weariness. Of course it's true that the spill could be seen coming from a long way back. But now that it *has* happened, it doesn't make me feel better to be able to say, "I told you so." I feel diminished. It's one more assault by this culture on the earth's fecundity. Having asphalted over the valleys, now we oil the seas and elbow the wild creatures a little further out of our way. Well, as Dad so eloquently stated, we seem to have things under control.

July 12

Back to work at South Beach. Some of the cleanup

workers look like automatons, stumbling along, raking and hauling in an oily despondency. The bird toll in the United States and Canada is now estimated at twenty thousand. An Audubon Society man was wondering today if the eagle population here on San Juan Island will suffer any harm from feeding on oiled fish that have washed up on shore. He pointed out that damage to bird populations is not just a matter of immediate kill, although that's one of the most obvious and irremediable effects of any oil spill. There's also the problem of food supply destroyed by the oil. Birds that usually land on one particular bay can't just pack up and move to the next bay, because there's probably just enough food in the next bay for the usual population. There may be a bird "shortage" in some places for a few years—shades of *Silent Spring*. Someone has figured out that the baling wire on the straw used so far for cleanup would reach thirty times around the state of Washington.

7

July 13
1:00 P.M.

While stepping off the Number 4 bus, pushing her way through the knapsacked crowds along University Way, climbing up the long flight of stairs to the office where she was about to interview Bill Wynette, Claudia Fitzsimmons brooded over injustice.

Now that the national media were on the scene —and everyone from the *New York Times* to *Rolling Stone* was here—her male editor at the *Seattle Times* had decided that Claudia should take a back seat. Women reporters were okay for in-depth, fourth-section backgrounders on major events, but the big front-page by-line stories were reserved for males. Of course the change of assignment hadn't been explained in that way. There was some mumbling about Claudia's having been with the *Times* for only two years, the need to get background, and so on. But Claudia knew what was up.

Well, she would show them. Let the men turn in the daily bird-casualty figures, and the latest crap from Octo and the Department of Ecology. That took a lot of brains, didn't it? She was going to do the best background articles on an oil spill that anyone had ever done, and when the big journalism awards were handed out, she'd be there. She had set up interviews with half the population of the Northwest, it seemed. She would talk to bigwigs, littlewigs and every wig in between. Wynette was one of Washington's leading conservationists and had been concerned with oil problems for several years. She was sure he'd be of use to her.

Wynette turned out to be short, stocky, bearded and rumpled. He led her away from the outer office where the phones never stopped ringing to a quieter, but messier, inner room. She wasted no time getting down to business.

"Why did this happen?" she asked.

"In one sentence?" Wynette responded. "Okay. Because of public apathy and ignorance, because of the power of the oil companies, because of the ignorance and gutlessness of many public officials."

"And yet," Claudia pointed out, "when there was a threat of underwater oil drilling in Puget Sound back in 1970, the public and government reacted right away—or so I've been told."

"That's right. Back when the state land commissioner wanted to raise some revenue by allowing drilling under the Sound, opposition poured in at once. Santa Barbara's big blowout of the year before was really on people's minds.

"The mayors and city councils of Edmonds and Tacoma, the two largest cities closest to proposed drilling sites, were strongly opposed. So were the state fisheries director, the state parks director, the Seattle City Council, the state oceanographic commission.

The fisheries director warned that spills from offshore drilling could wipe out the state's shellfish industry. He said it might take years to re-establish clam and oyster beds. One of our U.S. senators wrote a letter to the land commissioner asking about the effects of oil on tourism, fishing and boating. These enterprises, the senator said, are worth more than half a billion dollars a year to our state's economy. So drilling in Puget Sound is now banned under our Shorelines Management Act even if we may have to face it some day off the ocean coast. But oil damage is oil damage whether it comes from a drilling blowout or a tanker accident."

"Didn't the oil industry talk about 'failsafe' drilling the way it talks about 'failsafe' tankers?"

"Sure it did. But the drilling issue was resolved in too short a time for the industry to get fully mobilized. It came up, it was in the public limelight and it was a single-shot thing—one decision could settle it. One man, the land commissioner, had the power to decide whether leasing for drilling should proceed or not, although in the end he referred the decision to the State Board of Natural Resources for a vote.

"With tankers it's been different. Tankers have sailed on Puget Sound for many years and they just started getting bigger. There was no single person like the land commissioner who could say no to the big ones and make it stick. They were what the oil companies intended to use, and that was that.

"Our last governor, our present one, too, both took the position that the danger these big ships posed wasn't that great. All you had to do was get your traffic lanes and navigation aids and cleanup funds in order and everything would be dandy. A really big catastrophe was supposed to be highly unlikely.

"But as you and I both know, highly unlikely things happen all the time. The physicist George Weil gives two good examples in his booklet *Nuclear Energy: Promises, Promises.* He recalls the destruction by fire of Chicago's new convention hall a few years ago because of the automatic sprinkler system that was supposed to work but didn't. The president of one of the companies that had insured the place called it 'a fire that couldn't happen.' Or take the fire that killed the three astronauts in their Apollo spacecraft in 1967. The odds against that one were incredible. As a former reliability engineer by profession, I have some knowledge of the functioning of human systems. And I've become a believer in Murphy's Law: 'If something can go wrong, it will!'

"The point I always come back to is that with tankers, as with nuclear power plants, there's no such thing as zero risk. Now that we've seen the unthinkable happen, people are saying that any risk over zero is unacceptable. The same thing will happen if we ever have a nuclear meltdown. People will say, 'What were we doing all those years? How could we let this happen?'

"Then you have the oil and power-plant people preaching that the risk is worth taking. They mean that it's acceptable to them, the businesses that are making money off the operation. They make the decisions and the citizens take the risks—to their general welfare and even their personal health and safety. Forgive the preaching, but I'm really fired up."

"You must have said these things during the 1975

initiative campaign you ran. Why did it fail?"

"The usual reason. The oil industry is still the most powerful lobby around. Once we got into the campaign it was Proposition 18 all over again."

"What was Proposition 18?"

"That was the attempt in California, in 1970, to divert some highway tax monies to mass transit and air-pollution control. Even Ronald Reagan said he was for Proposition 18. The oil companies went all out to defeat it. They spent well over a quarter of a million bucks. Radio, TV and billboard messages claimed that passage of Proposition 18 would automatically mean higher taxes. Health groups, the League of Women Voters, conservationists spent about fifteen thousand dollars all told, countering this attack. You can guess who won.

"In our case, the oil industry spent more money to produce a twenty-seven-minute color movie than we had for our entire campaign. The film was called *Oil: Now, More Than Ever*. It opened with an old couple chopping wood. Then came a sonorous voice: 'There are always some people around who would like to return to the good old days, but for day-to-day living most of us would choose this,' and then they cut to an all-electric kitchen. 'It takes a lot of power to keep a city lit up at night,' the voice said, 'but it's better than this,' and they switch to a dark city skyline, a blackout, sirens wailing. 'It's a tough job these days keeping up with your demand for energy, but we've dedicated ourselves to that effort, however hard it gets,' and you see a picture of oil men drilling in a blizzard on the North Slope and being splashed with high waves in the Gulf of Mexico. 'We know you need oil now more than ever, and we believe in bringing it to you without damage to the environment we all depend on,' and they close with a picture of earth from outer space.

"Of course the film spewed forth all the usual industry cliches: alternative energy sources are far off in the future, energy conservation means major changes in life style, we need lots more energy for the poor and for pollution control. Many government reports and scholarly papers challenge these contentions, but scientists and professors don't have thousands of dollars to publish their research results in double-page color spreads in *Time Magazine*.

"Hell, just look at solar energy. The President's panel on solar energy reported in 1972 that widespread use of solar power is not some distant pie in the sky. This group of nearly forty experts in the field reported that with sufficient government support behind solar-energy programs, solar building heating could reach public use within five years, solar building cooling in six to ten years and solar electricity production in ten to fifteen years.

"Why, there are a couple dozen people around the country who are already running their homes on solar power and wind power. Some have been doing it for a number of years. People like Harry Thomason in Washington, D.C., Robert and Eileen Reines outside Albuquerque, Jim Sencenbaugh in California. And the National Audubon Society's new office building in Lincoln, Massachusetts, is using solar power as its main heating source.

"Sunlight's free. Maybe that's why you don't hear much about it in oil-company literature. Or take wind power: actually a type of solar power. Atlantic-Richfield ran a TV ad some time ago that showed a colorful old windmill with lights in its windows. As the windmill blades stopped going round, the lights went out in the windows and a voice said, 'A good idea—until the wind dies down.' Of course energy from the wind can be stored in batteries, and in many other ways. So why did ARCO run such an ad?

"William Heronemus, an engineering professor at the University of Massachusetts at Amherst, has calculated that a network of electricity-producing wind generators on the oceanic continental shelf of the northeastern United States could produce electricity for New England in 1990 at a cost per kilowatt hour lower than nukes or fossil-fueled power plants.

"Heronemus and more than thirty colleagues at the university proposed a national network of pollution-free energy sources using such things as ocean thermal-gradient heat engines, kinetic-energy machines and wind generators. In making a proposal for research funding to the National Science Foundation, the faculty members said that conservative calculations based on solid data demonstrated that the entire national energy requirement for the year 2000, both for electrical energy and direct fuel use, could be met by a limited group of nonpolluting energy sources.

"Heronemus and others have also suggested that we run our oil-gulping cars and trucks and buses on liquid hydrogen made by electrolyzing water and having it separate into hydrogen and oxygen. The hydrogen gas produced can be utilized in gas or liquid form. And if our cars were running on hydrogen, the air over our cities would be clean.

"There are so many interesting things going on in energy alternatives—often on shoestring budgets and often using ideas that have been around for years —that I've come to wonder whether we need our fossil fuels half as much as we think we do.

"There's trash power: burning municipal solid waste for fuel, as they're doing in St. Louis. There's plant power: growing algae and either burning the algae directly in conventional power plants or fermenting algae to produce methane—natural gas.

"There's ocean power: building floating sea-thermal power plants that operate on the temperature differences between deep, cold ocean water and warmer surface waters. A well known engineer in turbomachinery, James Anderson, Sr., has said that the heat in the Gulf Stream alone would easily supply power for the entire eastern half of the United States. It's an old idea, and Anderson says that we have the materials, technology and machinery to build these plants right now. And he says they would produce electricity more cheaply than any known power plant!

"Then there's my favorite power source: fuel made from shit. In 1970 the Department of the Interior put out a little-publicized study saying that the domestic animals in this country—cattle, chickens, pigs— produce enough waste every year to make two billion barrels of low-sulfur oil, almost 40 per cent of the United States' oil consumption in 1973. This is another thing we already know how to do. A panel of energy experts reported in 1972 to the Office of Science and Technology that at least 30 per cent of gaseous fuel and 10 per cent of future oil requirements for the United States could be met by this production process.

"The real question in energy, as I see it, is whether we can move into some of these cleaner, safer energy alternatives before we've destroyed what's left of our wilderness areas, our fisheries resources, our farmlands; before we've strip-mined Montana and oil-shaled Colorado and had a nuclear meltdown in Illinois. And—maybe the most important thing of all—before we've tied our energy economy to the fast-breeder reactor. That one has many scientists scared to death.

"As people have pointed out, the problems here are not technological or even economic; they're political. Because of certain political forces, for example, we spent nearly three billion dollars of taxpayers' money on civilian nuclear-energy programs between 1954 and 1972, and only one million dollars for work on large-scale solar-power systems. Think where we might be today if it had been the other way around.

"And think about some of these energy sources in relation to national security and balance-of-payment problems. No dollar outflows, no Arab blackmail, with sun power and shit power! So why are we taking so long to get to it? You can't talk about tankers and offshore drilling and offshore leasing and all the rest of it without looking at the much larger spectrum of the total energy issue."

"What exactly did your 1975 initiative propose?"

"It declared a moratorium on the entry into Puget Sound of tankers over fifty thousand deadweight tons. We felt that the threat to the health and welfare of the people of the state from supertanker operation was such that we could win in court if the moratorium were challenged as interference with interstate commerce."

"Then you were trying to ban supertankers that were of pretty moderate size."

"If the whole thing's relative, yes. But I don't think it is. Some people like to argue that a 'supertanker' ten years ago meant a ship of *Grand Canyon* size, but today means a ship two or three times bigger. But the fact that somebody builds a bigger skyscraper in Chicago doesn't make the Empire State Building a shoebox. A *Grand Canyon* is one hell of a big ship.

"Ships that size started coming into Puget Sound in 1972, headed for the ARCO refinery north of Bellingham. That refinery was designed for Alaskan oil, but since no one foresaw all the difficulties that lay in the way of the Alaska pipeline, it was completed long before the pipeline started flowing. So oil for the refinery was brought in by supertanker from the Middle East.

"In those days, the big ships didn't come in very often; about once a month, say. Once a week, what we've got now, didn't sound like much either. It sounded rather soothing. So did the frequent reminders that Washington and Oregon—supposedly the logical, limited marketing area for oil refined in Washington—had small populations and would not require tremendous refinery expansion and the concomitant increases in tanker traffic. There just weren't that many people out here, we were told, and oil tends to be refined close to marketing areas for reasons of transportation cost.

"Such thinking overlooked the fact that the idea of

a pipeline from Seattle to Chicago kept coming up over and over again. Former Governor Evans used to say that a trans-Cascade pipeline was a development that *would* worry him, because he knew it would mean greatly increased amounts of oil on our waters. Puget Sound would take all the risks of spills and get nothing in return. Personally, I've met few Seattleites who like Chicago enough to ruin the San Juans for it.

"Aside from a crude-oil pipeline east, there are plenty of businessmen around who have suggested that Puget Sound become a major oil-refining and petrochemical center for the country. The Seattle-King County Economic Development Council has been tantalized by such notions. As you know, no area of the United States can compare with Puget Sound when it comes to the water depths needed for big ships. Just the natural conditions afford a certain invitation, give people archaic notions about how to deal with local unemployment problems.

"Some people say I'm anti-industry, but I say let's have the kinds of industry that our area is suited for. We have a tourist industry that is moving into number-three spot in economic importance to our state; it's expected to be number one by the year 2000. More than half of that industry centers on the Puget Sound area. People come here from all over the country to catch a salmon, and almost one in three of Washington's residents does some sport fishing. We have a boat-building industry and more pleasure-boat owners than any other part of the United States; there are about 200 thousand pleasure boats in the Puget Sound area. We have public officials who have expressed their desire to see more and more oceanographic research facilities here, and others who have spoken of a $100-million aquaculture industry in the next ten years. You can either go into these things, or you can go into petrochemicals and refineries. In my view the last thing we need to do on Puget Sound is recreate Bayonne, New Jersey, or Gary, Indiana.

"Even without major refinery and petrochemical development, the Army Corps of Engineers has predicted that Puget Sound will have to triple its present refining capacity by the year 2000 to keep up with local market demand, which means expansion of some present refineries and probably one new one. And more oil on our waters. More oil, more ship traffic of all kinds—you can see what the pressures are. Honeywell Marine Systems Center concluded in a study they did back in 1970 that Puget Sound could expect anywhere from three to six tanker accidents from collisions or groundings over the following ten years, depending on the rate of traffic growth.

"The corps made a big thing in its 1973 West Coast superport study about how using a few big tankers rather than lots of smaller ones for carrying crude would reduce the odds on accidents and make our local waters cleaner in the 1980's than they would otherwise be. But if you take a look at some numerical evaluation charts they've come up with, you find that by the year 2000 Washington's waters will be getting dirtier even by following the corps' own strategy. It's just a matter of the volume of oil handled.

"If we really want to save our waters, we've got to get going on better transportation systems. Two thirds of the oil consumed in Washington goes for transportation. There's a direct connection between the big under-utilized cars on our highways and the possible end of our salmon runs.

"We should be looking for ways to keep that new refinery from ever being built. In terms of present state and federal law, the machinery for doing that doesn't look good.

"But we don't have to have all that oil. When a local corporation like Boeing can cut its energy consumption by 20 per cent without layoffs or cutbacks in production, you can see how much fat there is in the system.

"Back in 1972, the United States Office of Emergency Preparedness produced a study that found that moderate energy-conservation measures—improved insulation in homes, building more efficient air conditioners, moving freight by rail rather than truck, getting people out of their cars and into mass-transit systems, improving the efficiency of industrial processes and equipment —could save the equivalent of 7.3 million barrels of oil per day by 1980. That figure equals about two thirds of the projected oil imports for that year. When you look at the 'need' for the Alaska pipeline in the light of a study like that, it's sort of a joke. And yet only twenty-nine of the 100 members of the United States Senate were willing to stand up on the key vote in Congress and say that they were not being stampeded into anything. Only twenty-nine out of 100 voted for an amendment to the pipeline bill which provided for a twelve-month study by the National Academy of Sciences to find out what was really the best way to bring out the oil from Prudhoe Bay.

"Very few people were aware, for example, that a railroad-transport system down the MacKenzie River Valley through Canada had been studied by faculty members at American and Canadian universities and found technically and economically feasible. Not to mention environmentally safer than the trans-Alaska pipeline. But no; everything was rush, rush, rush. There never was a better example of the power of the oil companies than the fight over the Alaska pipeline. I was in Washington, D. C. at the time, and I remember what one embittered Midwesterner said after the House voted to exempt the pipeline project from the requirements of the National Environmental Policy Act: 'It was a shameful afternoon. The whole House stank of oil.' "

Claudia asked, "How did you respond to the argument that having a few big ships around is better than having lots of smaller ones? Doesn't that assertion have some validity?"

"Well, the basic idea there, of course, is that accidents occur in relation to the number of ships, so the fewer ships, the fewer collisions. But as the Maritime Administration points out in the final Environmental Impact Statement on its supertanker construction program, the big ships are less maneuverable than the small ones; they're built badly underpowered, with stopping distances measured in miles, so you have to consider that.

"Brand-new supertankers coming out of shipyards in the early 70's—the *Grand Canyon* is a case in point—did not have adequate horsepower or the best possible maneuvering equipment. For a short time in the autumn of 1973, during the weeks that a Congressional conference committee was working on the Alaska pipeline bills, the local news media gave the impression that such ships might be banned from

Puget Sound. But when Congress finished its work, it hadn't happened.

"The Coast Guard has all the legal authority it needs to do something about tanker standards under the Ports and Waterways Safety Act of 1972, but they're subject to the usual pressures and haven't done what they could. Looking to international agencies hasn't been much use, either. At the big Intergovernmental Maritime Consultative Organization meeting in London, in November of 1973, there was even a danger for a while that the nations present would draw up a convention that would prevent the signatory powers from setting up within individual nations tanker-construction standards that were stricter than what the powers represented would agree to. And the powers represented wouldn't agree to much of anything, not even double bottoms. The American delegation favored them, but many other countries didn't.

"So there you are. Inferior maneuvering capacity isn't so serious when you're out on the open ocean and have time to activate your emergency steering apparatus. But in narrow waters like ours, where the shore or a big rock may be only minutes away, you've had it.

"The Oceanographic Institute of Washington, in its 1973 study of oil transportation and handling, pointed out that the rocks and shoals in Rosario Strait are potential grounding hazards. The institute also expressed worry that the entrances to the Strait, bounded by various rocks and islands, are especially hazardous for situations when ships meet because those entrances have only restricted space for ships to maneuver. Haro Strait, the other main shipping route, has some very bad places, too."

"What was the vote in the initiative election?"

"We got a 41 per cent Yes vote. Considering what we were up against, it wasn't too bad. . . . "

They went on talking. The big clock on the wall soon said 2:15 P.M.

North of Fort Lawton, the injured *Grand Canyon* was being pulled south by two tugs, the *Sea Empress* and the *Jupiter*.

After eleven days of sweating and swearing, a salvage crew had finished enough pumping and repair work for the ship to be towed into drydock at Bremerton. At daybreak steel hawsers had been attached to the tanker, and four tugboats pulling together had freed the ship from Bird Rocks. Two of the tugs then loosed themselves, and the crippled ship seemed ready for her journey.

Unfortunately, there were problems. As though reluctant to return to sea duty, the tanker refused to tow in a straight line. The salvage master decided that some ballasting was necessary to correct her veering motion, so an hour south of Bird Rocks the tugs stopping pulling and the pumping of ballast water began. When this operation was finally finished, and after one pump had broken down and been replaced, the tow was resumed. Slowly the ship was drawn through the glassy aquamarine waters south of the spill area. The *Sea Empress* and the *Jupiter* headed for Seattle.

And then, at 2:15 P.M., something happened that no one had foreseen. With a great boom that made dishes rattle in cupboards on Magnolia Bluff, the *Grand*

[95]

Canyon suddenly cracked across the center. Her Coast Guard escort watched in helpless horror as the tanker's back and front halves separated. A vast wave of water rushed away from the broken ship. And Alaskan crude began to pour into lower Puget Sound.

8

July 13
6:15 P.M.
Seattle Municipal Building, twelfth floor

"All right. We're all here, and now, I hope, gentlemen, that someone can tell me what the hell is going
on." Seattle's mayor, August L. "Gus" Rahm, nodded
curtly to Lambert Bibb, who had just been ushered in.
The door closed gently behind him.

It was exactly four hours after the *Grand Canyon* had
broken in half off Fort Lawton. Already assembled in the
mayor's offices were Coast Guard Captain Verrill Albright, captain of the Port of Seattle; Harry Kirschner, an
oceanographer from the University of Washington;
Oran Jensen; and Joseph Bernik, general manager of the
Port of Seattle and long-time member of the city's business establishment. The mayor's administrative assis-
tant, Roger Tanaka, sat with a yellow pad ready to make
notes. Bibb sat down next to Bernik on the black leather
sofa in front of Mayor Rahm's desk.

Rahm came around from behind his desk and sat on it,
the picture of the vigorous young man of last year's election campaign. "There's an oil slick three miles long
just a stone's throw from West Point," he said. "I'm told

it now fills up half the channel between there and Bain-bridge Island. We're all going to be late for dinner, gentlemen, but there were at last count seventeen reporters out there—" he pointed toward the waiting room—"and the switchboard is jammed with calls from all over the city. They want answers. I want answers. You, presumably, have some answers. I want the straight story on what happened. Captain Albright?"

Albright, straightbacked and uniformed, frowned at his clipboard. "The Coast Guard escort to the towing operation reports that she simply came apart at the seams; the tanker, that is, sir," he said in his Kentucky drawl. "Cracked open right across the centerline. The bow half of the ship, which was empty of oil, sank. The stern half, which was attached to the tow lines, had one of its centerline tanks ripped open. That's the source of the oil slick, sir."

"How much oil has spilled?"

Albright closed his eyes. "If it's the whole centerline tank, it might be more than five million gallons."

"Five million gallons!"

"That's the maximum that could be lost," Lambert Bibb interrupted. "In all likelihood it's a great deal less than that."

"The stern of the tanker has been towed to Bremer-ton," Albright said, "and they're offloading the rest of the oil."

"Why in God's name wasn't all the oil taken out of the ship before you brought her south?"

"It was a reasonable decision," Jensen said. "It takes time to offload all the oil in a ship that big, and she was getting ground up pretty badly out there from tidal currents rubbing her against the rocks. The idea was to take out as much oil as was needed to get her free—and we took a lot out—and then bring her into drydock before she broke up on Bird Rocks."

"Every reasonable precaution was taken," Captain Albright said. "The procedure was thoroughly checked over by every agency involved."

"The salvage master was the best in the business," Bibb said. "This is a one-in-a-million accident. There is no way it could have been foreseen."

"There is no way it could have been foreseen. All precautions were taken. The decisions were reasonable," Rahm repeated. "Yet now there's something like five million gallons of crude oil hanging off the city. If you open the window you can smell it." He paused. "Needless to say, gentlemen, we don't want that oil coming ashore in Seattle. What do you propose to do about it? Mr. Bibb, is Octogon accepting the responsibility?"

Bibb hesitated, then nodded. "Under state law, it's up to us to deal with the oil. Normally we'd hire a contractor to carry out the cleanup, but since our contractor is totally involved up north, we've asked the Department of Ecology to take direct control for mobilization of equipment and everything else."

"As predesignated on-scene coordinator," Captain Albright interjected, "I have already taken certain steps. I have drawn on the thirty-million-dollar revolving fund and have activated the national contingency plan to oversee the monitoring and removal of the oil as the situation dictates."

"Does that mean you're in charge?" Rahm asked.

Albright began to answer in the affirmative, but Oran Jensen spoke up quickly. "Actually, the Department of Ecology has full authority," he said.

"But if these new conditions should be beyond the state's capability," Albright said, "or if the governor gets disaster relief funds, that means federal authority."

Rahm stood up. "All right, just whose God-damn authority is it?" he said. "I would think that after all these years of writing contingency plans someone would at least know who's in charge."

Jensen's face twitched with weariness. He would never hear the last of it from his director if he gave in to the idea of federal responsibility. "Ecology's staff has been working for two weeks up north and we have the expertise," he said. "We have the authority, as spelled out in the 1976 state oil-spill contingency plan."

"I am the *federal* on-scene coordinator," Captain Albright said with dignity. "If Mr. Jensen intends to take charge for the state of Washington, he can kindly do so."

"No reason why we can't cooperate," Jensen said hastily. "The Coast Guard's assistance with boats and helicopters will be much appreciated."

"Our job is to do our utmost to mitigate any harmful effects," Albright said, subsiding.

"All right," said Rahm, "where is the oil going to go?"

"We have a fair idea," Jensen said. "Professor Kirschner has a physical model of the lower Sound at the U.W. that simulates currents and tides. As soon as I got the exact location of the spill pinpointed, I called Harry and asked him to drop some dye into the model to see where it would go. Harry?"

Kirschner, who so far had not said a word, brought his chart over to the mayor's desk. "Let me explain first how our model works," he said. "It's like a very big bathtub, except that it's shaped to the topography of the lower Sound: everything south of Admiralty Inlet. We have water in the model, and we have ways of adjusting it for different times of year, different mixes of salt and fresh water, and so forth. To get a reading, we crank in some of the variables, then drop in blue dye to represent a spill. Then we watch where it goes.

"I should point out that our model has no way of taking wind conditions into account. These affect oil movements too. But if the weather remains as it is —sunny with very gentle winds of about five knots—we should be not too far off.

"Now," he said, and began to mark the chart rapidly with a black felt pen, "limits of heavy impact will be, roughly, Edmonds at the north and the northern tip of Vashon Island on the south." Rahm watched in growing alarm as the black pen traveled along the Seattle shoreline. "Here are some places in Seattle that are likely to be hit," Kirschner continued. "Golden Gardens, Shilshole, the Fort Lawton tidelands, Elliott Bay, Alki Point, the beaches of the Fauntleroy area. On the other side of the channel: Indianola, Suquamish, Winslow and shorelines behind Agate Passage, on Port Orchard and Liberty Bay. Areas beyond these, I would say, may be affected later on as slicks circulate and break into smaller patches."

"Professor Kirschner, how soon would you expect oil to touch shore?"

"West Point will be the first area in Seattle, right here along Perkins Lane," Kirschner said. "That should be tomorrow morning. The main slick will gradually fill up the whole channel, but it won't actually reach Golden Gardens, Shilshole and Carkeek Park until the next day, Saturday. By then it will also be across the whole harbor entrance to Elliott Bay and down to Alki. And on Sunday, it will be coming into Elliott Bay itself in the vicinity of Pier 90 and Pier 91. I'm surprised, actually, that the oil may take that long to work into Elliott Bay, but that's what the model says. It's a very complex current situation out there."

There was silence as the others absorbed his words.

"I can't believe it," Joe Bernik said. "That much oil in Elliott Bay—we've never considered anything like that. We've never considered it."

"Three days, Jensen," Rahm said. "Less than that. What are you going to do? Can you put a boom across Elliott Bay?"

"Gus," said Bernik, "I trust it will not be necessary to close the port. This port has never been closed by anything but labor. We handle over nine million dollars' worth of cargo every day, and the ships won't wait. Tomorrow we're expecting seven large container ships."

Jensen was doubtful. "It's more than two miles from Duwamish Head to Pier 90. I doubt that a boom that long could stand up, even with slow currents. It would almost certainly snap."

"Can you set fire to the oil?" the mayor asked.

Bernik winced. "Think of the fire hazard!"

Jensen agreed with Bernik. "Too close to shore. And chemical dispersants are out, too, for biological reasons," he said.

"The hell with biology!" Rahm said. "Keep it off the shorelines!"

"Oran is right," Kirschner put in. "The comparatively

poor flushing action this far south in the Sound, along with the harmful ingredients in the chemicals themselves, could create a biological disaster."

Rahm stood up and paced toward the window. "Damn it, Jensen!" he said. "Seattle prides itself on being a livable city. We're talking about oil at the waterfront park and aquarium, oil in front of the Edgewater Hotel, oil at Ivar's Acres of Clams, oil at the ferry landings—— " He went on, conjuring up a vision of a Seattle waterfront suffocating for weeks under an odoriferous onslaught of sticky crude. "Oil on boats, oil below Magnolia Bluff, oil at the fishing docks, oil at Lincoln Park." He looked around the room. No one had anything to say.

Rahm sat down again. "So we can't stop the oil from coming into Seattle," he said. "I see." He turned to Bibb. "Failsafe tankers, radar control, vast cleanup arsenal —horseshit. This is the worst disaster to hit Seattle since the fire. Are you going to mop this up with your press releases?"

Bibb sat for a moment twisting a cuff link back and forth. Then, looking levelly back at the mayor, he said, "I'm sorry you feel that way. Octogon has always been a good corporate citizen. And speaking personally, I am just as emotionally upset by this accident as you or anyone else. Just this morning I was out on a beach with Octo's research team, looking at heaps of sick clams and rotting crabs and sea worms. Believe me, it's not a pretty sight.

"But I try to keep things in perspective. Values. I remind myself that there has been no loss of human life, thank God. I remind myself that America runs on oil, and that the services provided by Octogon in making

Alaskan oil available are essential to our economy and our way of life. I thought we all accepted that."

"I see no reason to single out Octogon, Gus," Bernik said with a note of reproach. He had known Bibb through business connections for years. "They were unlucky. Unfortunately, their bad luck is ours, too. But it could have been any oil company."

"Maybe that's the point," Rahm said. "But let's skip it. I've got a press release of my own to write." He looked at Oran Jensen, who had started making notes on the back of an envelope. "You must have one or two ideas on how to soften the blow, Jensen," he said. "Let's hear them."

Jensen, relieved to see the end of the meeting approaching, warmed to the practical task of planning. "We'll do what we can for Seattle," he said, "if we can find some skimmers and booms to do some corralling, but the trouble is that every skimmer on the West Coast is already working up north. We're going to have to bring in equipment from Houston this time, by air. The straw supply is even more of a problem; we were running low as it was. As soon as I leave, I'll get on the phone to the state ecology people in Illinois—we're going to have to draw on the Midwest. Frankly, I don't see that Elliott Bay has top priority, do you?"

"Well, if we have to make a choice—" Rahm was hesitant, aware of the political risk in assigning more value to one part of the city than another. "It's true that our good beaches aren't in there," he said. "It's all industrial or fill or piers that are creosoted anyway. We're going to hear a lot more about Golden Gardens."

"We can't do much for Golden Gardens in advance," Jensen said. "It's straight exposed coast. But we can try to have straw and crews ready to sop oil up as it comes in. We can boom off the ends of the Shilshole breakwater to protect the boats in there."

"There's one boom that's already in place, at least," Captain Albright said.

"What's that?"

"The ship locks into Salmon Bay. The locks themselves will keep oil from going in. And when the locks have to be opened for ship traffic, fresh water will pour out and flush the area in front for five or six hundred feet."

"I think we can also try running booms perpendicular to the shoreline from West Point to Pier 90," Jensen said. "That's just for oil-collecting purposes. As the water moves along parallel to the shore, oil will pile up against the booms. Then if we can find some skimmers—or pumps! I'll call the septic-tank services. We can use their suction pumps to collect the oil."

"Roger, have you got things down?" the mayor asked his aide. "All right. Let's get with the program. I'll have the fire department patrol the shorelines in case any oil is accidentally ignited. We'll issue a general request to the public to keep waterfront activity to a minimum while Jensen and Albright set up their gear."

"No ban on port shipping, then?" Bernik said.

Rahm looked to Jensen.

"We saw no reason to restrict ship movements up north except in boomed harbors," Jensen said. "If they want to oil their hulls, let them. The Winslow ferry may be a problem, though. We'll be under heavy pressure from property owners to boom off Eagle Harbor, but we'll be under equal pressure to keep commuter service open."

"Keep the ferries running," Rahm said. "Let's try to maintain some semblance of normal routine. You all understand that I expect to be kept fully informed of everything that happens or might happen that affects this city. I hope that's clear."

The meeting broke up. Oran Jensen and Harry Kirschner bent over the chart discussing currents, Captain Albright was off to Coast Guard headquarters, Bibb invited Bernik to join him for dinner and Roger Tanaka was calmly drafting a statement for the reporters waiting impatiently in the outer office.

Mayor Rahm prepared to give his constituents a lot of bad news.

9

July 13
9:30 P.M.

"Good evening. This is Bill McGowan for Channel Four. You've just heard a taped message from Mayor Gus Rahm on the second *Grand Canyon* catastrophe, asking everyone to keep calm and cooperate fully with state and federal authorities.

"Now I'd like to welcome you to this special live broadcast. With us in the studio tonight to discuss the spill are Professor Thomas Hatcher, marine biologist from Huxley College in Bellingham; naval architect James Washburn; and Lambert Bibb, vice-president of Octogon Oil's Western Division. Mr. Washburn, what actually happened to that ship out there this afternoon?"

"Well, we won't really know the full details until the Coast Guard conducts the official inquiry, but from what I've been able to learn, it seems that once the tugs got the *Grand Canyon* off the rocks and began pulling her south, she was a bad tow. That is, she wouldn't pull along in a straight line.

"Remember that her whole front half was empty, either because of oil tanks torn up when she grounded or because of the offloading needed to get her loose. The tugs were pulling from the stern of the ship and the vessel keept veering in an **S** pattern behind the tugs. So the salvage master decided he would have to put some ballast water in her to add enough weight to control the problem.

"The tugs stopped pulling and the salvage crew went to work pumping water into those tanks near the bow that weren't punctured. These would have been, I believe, the number-one and number-two starboard wing tanks. Then the tow was resumed.

"The veering problem was corrected, but apparently the weight of that much ballast water all on one side set up longitudinal stresses that the ship just couldn't take. She held up as far as Fort Lawton and then she just let go amidships—cracked open right across the middle.

"There was a case of another tanker giving way to stresses and splitting in two like the *Grand Canyon* in Port Jefferson Harbor on Long Island in 1972. In that case the ship had been completely unloaded, but the *Grand Canyon* still had oil aboard in the number-three centerline tank, and that oil was all released by the break-up."

"Was there no way that the salvage master could have foreseen that the ballasting would crack her? Suppose he had put less weight on that one side?"

"It's pretty hard to predict anything like that. Most likely the ship started cracking in some place where she had already sustained side damage, or where there was a crack that had developed since her last drydock inspection. The salvage master couldn't know about that. I think he made a decision that looked perfectly reasonable at the time."

"So everything that was done was perfectly reasonable, and yet the result was this incredible mess?"

"I'm not saying the whole operation wasn't risky. As I said, break-ups are not unknown. To my mind, the thing that was most unreasonable was letting a ship that big into Puget Sound in the first place. An underpowered tanker 880 feet long is too unwieldy for these narrow waters—navigating it is comparable to navigating a forty-five-foot boat with a one-third-horsepower motor. But Puget Sound has the water depths for a tanker that big and for much bigger ones. That's a great attraction for oil commerce, and it's one reason why we're here tonight. If you have to have tankers of over fifty thousand tons in use, they should be kept well out to sea for docking, off the open coast. Or at least brought no further in than Port Angeles, where it's possible to build a port with ship locks and underwater pipelines to our inland refineries."

"Uh—if I could just make a point here."

"Yes, Mr. Bibb?"

"I'd like to point out that if you don't use big ships you've got to use a lot more smaller ones to bring in the same amount of oil. And the more ships there are running around, the more collisions—and spills—you're likely to have."

"Mr. Washburn, would you care to comment on that?"

"Well, for one thing, that doesn't answer the question of where you bring the ships. Some places, as I've just said, are a lot more suitable than the inner waters of Puget Sound. But for another thing, when you bring in the big ones, you set yourselves up for a big accident. Common sense tells you that a ship that holds only six million gallons, like the old T-2's used to, can't spill thirteen million gallons—or more.

"Finally, we shouldn't fall into the trap of thinking that this state is limited only to options having to do with ships. If the oil companies ever decide to build a pipeline from Alaska across Canada—the one they might have built to begin with—Washington could tap into that for its state oil supply."

"Mr. Bibb, what would be your response to that?"

"I think that depends on whether you take a narrow, local view of the energy problem or whether you realize that the energy problem is so important to our society and our way of life that it has to be viewed from a national perspective. We can't just think about the oil needs of the state of Washington—other states need oil also. And here in Puget Sound you have the ideal natural conditions for a major oil-importing center serving the needs of the whole country."

"Mr. Bibb, I notice that Octo's stock closed somewhat lower than usual on tonight's exchange. Would you connect that with this second disaster?"

"I really couldn't say, Bill, and I think we should reserve judgment on whether or not we call this a disaster. As you know, other areas that have been hit by big oil spills have come through with little damage in the end. Take Santa Barbara, for instance—people's worst fears were just not justified. The immediate impact I'll grant is bound to be unpleasant, but I wouldn't want Seattle's residents to become unduly alarmed."

"Well, the volumes don't really compare to Santa Barbara, do they? First we had the Sound getting hit with eight million gallons up north; now we've got five million gallons loose down here. This is by far the biggest oil spill in United States history, whether it's labelled a disaster or not. I seem to recall that Santa Barbara was only 250 thousand gallons. Is that right, Professor Hatcher?''

"That's the figure that's usually given for the initial blowout, Bill. Actually, there was a great deal more subsequent leakage and the total spillage is still a matter of dispute. But I'd like to hear Mr. Bibb go on television in Santa Barbara and say that the big 1969 blowout wasn't a disaster. He'd probably be run out of town on a rail. The public outcry there cut across all shades of political opinion and united the community as nothing in its history had before.''

"I was speaking only of the long-term biological effects when I said it was not a disaster. One often finds that these are overstated.''

"If what you mean by that is that there's still plenty of sealife off the coast of Santa Barbara, that is correct. Thank God Mother Nature is resilient; she needs to be. We probably never will know how much harm the 1969 blowout did, because the studies done afterward were not as sophisticated as they should have been. And Santa Barbara was lucky in one respect. Its blowout came in the middle of winter—in January—at a time when sea plants and other organisms are in a dormant, less vulnerable state than during growing seasons. In comparison with our area, Santa Barbara waters are much less confined and they're warmer. Both of these factors are an advantage in recovering from the destructive effects of a spill. The point I really want to make is that each particular oil spill is unique. We really can't know right now what the biological consequences of this spill are going to be, because so many factors are

[111]

involved. But the 1969 Buzzards Bay spill near West Falmouth, Massachusetts, is the one I think about the most."

"That Buzzards Bay spill always seems to come up when people talk about oil. Would you explain that incident to our viewers, Dr. Hatcher?"

"Be glad to, Bill. As you know, oil pollution used to be thought of as a matter of dirty beaches and a lot of dead birds. People thought it was okay to eat seafood from a spill area as long as it didn't smell or taste oily, and they thought that oil and water don't mix, that oil just floats on the surface, so you go out and chase it with skimmer boats and bring it back.

"All of these popular beliefs were thrown into question by work done at the Woods Hole Oceanographic Institution by Dr. Max Blumer and his associates. One foggy night in September of 1969, a fuel barge went aground on submerged rocks in Buzzards Bay near Cape Cod. The radar on the tugboat pulling the barge had failed, and the rudder and tow line broke. Diesel oil covered beaches and washed into marshes. Scientists from Woods Hole went to work studying the oil's effect on the local shellfish, bottomfish and other sealife.

"Fortunately for their study, this was an area where much research had already been done; in other words, there were base lines for comparative purposes. They watched the marine-animal population decline, in the course of a week or so, from close to 200,000 live animals per square meter to about 2 live animals per square meter. And the amount of oil spilled was only 180 thousand gallons—very little compared to what we are facing here now.

"Using sophisticated methods of chemical analysis,

Blumer and other scientists found that the oil spilled in Buzzards Bay had contaminated the bottom sediments—that it had mixed into the water column and found its way to the sea bottom. In the immediate area where the spill occurred there was, of course, a massive kill. It became a biological desert. But what's more, the desert spread. Without the bottom grasses and animals to hold things in place, the sea bottom began to move. As the months went by, oil on the bottom was carried by wave action and shifting of sediments over an ever larger area, and everywhere it went, the kill continued. In six months, the polluted area had expanded tenfold. And this was long after any visual trace of oil remained on nearby shorelines. So natural bacterial action to degrade the oil must have been very slow."

"Thank you, Professor Hatcher. Let's stop here; I think we are ready for some questions phoned in by our viewers. We've had to be selective in choosing questions. I understand that our switchboard has been busier tonight than at any time in the history of the station.

"Here's a caller who says that the Santa Barbara blowout didn't destroy commercial fishing down there in California, any more than the Chevron oil-well blowouts in the Gulf of Mexico in 1970 wiped out fishing in the Gulf. In fact, this person says, fishermen in the Gulf are pulling in more fish than ever. Who would like to respond to that? Dr. Hatcher?"

"Those fish-landing statistics are notoriously difficult to interpret. The adult fish being landed may not have spent much time in a polluted area. Shellfish are better indicators of damage. And this takes me back to Buzzards Bay again. There, shellfish beds were ordered closed to harvesting for more than two years. It was found that oysters exposed to the diesel oil, when transferred to clean water, could not clean themselves. In other words, oil that had entered their flesh was not degraded.

"This raised the prospect that oil hydrocarbons might, like DDT and other persistent substances, be passed up the ocean food chains when contaminated organisms were eaten by others that might have been far from the spill area at the time the spill occurred. Another discovery was that juvenile mussels affected by the oil were found to be sterile when they reached maturity the next year."

"You wanted to add something here, Mr. Bibb?"

"I'd just like to mention, Bill, that all these harmful effects Mr. Hatcher mentions came from refined oil —diesel oil. Crude is less toxic than refined products, and after a few days' aging the part that has not evaporated is readily consumed by bacteria."

"Professor Hatcher, what about that?"

"This is a complete misunderstanding. I'm surprised Mr. Bibb is not aware of the extensive research done by the oil industry itself on this topic. The basic components of refined petroleum products are derived from the original crude oil. All crudes and all refined products—except for some highly purified materials —contain substances that can be poisonous to marine life. Some of these substances cause immediate death, others have a slower effect.

"Speaking generally, crude oil is less immediately toxic on an equal-weight basis than some refined products, but it contains more of the longer-lasting long-term poisons. Even in crude that has weathered for some time, many of the acutely toxic hydrocarbons still persist. As for evaporation, its significance has been exaggerated. Under certain conditions petroleum will sink as readily as it will evaporate. This is what happened at Falmouth. Once the oil got into bottom sediments, it was apparently hard for bacteria to degrade it. And bacteria attack the least toxic fractions of oil first, leaving plenty of opportunity for the more toxic fractions to be taken up by marine organisms."

"Here's a related question, Dr. Hatcher: is it true that eating clams or oysters from oil-polluted beaches will give you cancer?"

"There's not a *yes* or a *no* on that, Bill. Oil does contain substances that have produced cancer in laboratory animals. Some years back, it was noticed that oil-refinery workers were contracting a higher than normal share of skin cancer, and this was traced to prolonged skin contact with oil and oil products. So we do have to be concerned about a possible health hazard. We need more research in this area, but, as things stand now, I think it would be stupid to eat seafood you knew had oil in it. And remember, just because a clam doesn't taste or smell oily doesn't mean there's no oil in it.

"Incidentally, some recent work indicates another problem with oil: it may act as a concentrator of other fat-soluble poisons such as insecticides. So a limpet feeding on oil-contaminated algae, say, may be getting not only a dose of oil, but also a dose of DDT dissolved in the oil. And may pass it on to us, eventually."

"Thanks, Dr. Hatcher. Let's take another question. A viewer wants to know whether a double bottom or twin screw propellers on the *Grand Canyon* would have prevented the initial tragedy up on Bird Rocks. That's for you, Mr. Washburn."

"Generally, I'd say double bottoms are highly desirable. But in this case a double bottom would have helped only a little, because the bottom penetrations were too deep—over five meters in three of the four tanks affected. The grounding virtually impaled her on the rocks. But twin screw propellers might have prevented the whole thing."

"Is that right?"

"Yes. You see, Bill, if a ship has two propellers, rather than one, like the *Grand Canyon*, she can use them to steer if she should lose rudder steerage. You put one propeller on forward and one on reverse, and the ship will turn."

"In other words, all we need to do is build our supertankers right and they'll be risk-free?"

"No, I don't want to leave that impression. It just happens that in this one case twin screw propellers might have prevented the accident. But there are so many ways accidents can happen that the only certain way to prevent supertanker accidents in Puget Sound is to not let supertankers in. I would certainly agree that if you do let them in, double bottoms and twin screw propellers should be minimum requirements for reducing risks."

"Thank you, gentlemen. On that note we'll conclude this program. Stay tuned for a late report on the movement of the oil. Please do *not* call the station for information on cleanup or bird-rescue plans. We will flash this information throughout the evening as soon as it is available."

July 15
6:00 P.M.

"This is Ralph Inniss for Channel Seven. I'm standing here at Meadow Point in Golden Gardens. Ordinarily, people come here in the summer to cultivate their tans, scuba dive, read, neck, throw sticks for their dogs, beachcomb, picnic under the trees, stroll, sleep, or steal sand from the sandiest beach you'll find in Seattle. None of those activities are going on here now. There are plenty of people here, all right, but they're all doing the same thing—trying to pick up the black gooey mess that came into Golden Gardens today. We've got a stiff breeze here, and around Meadow Point to the north the waves really pounded the oil in. Someone has put up a big sign renaming the beach STP Estates. There seem to be students here from every school in Seattle, but it's not just young people trying to clean up this favorite Seattle beach. There are people here of all ages working together against the common enemy, oil. This spirit of unity and cooperation might be considered a small positive gain in compensation for having to look at the dead clams and the dead mussels and the dead birds and this coated, dying octopus that washed ashore a few moments ago. This is Ralph Inniss for Channel Seven."

"This is Nick Remick. I'm standing here on Pier A at the Shilshole Bay Marina, where one of those freak incidents occurred late last night which always seem to accompany major disasters. A pleasure cruiser wanting to get inside the protected area ahead of the oil ran in and cut right through the permeable mesh boom which was supposed to protect the marina. In the darkness no one noticed that the boom was no longer in place, so oil is into the marina, coating the hulls of these very beautiful and expensive yachts here in front of me. Because of the possible fire danger, the Coast Guard has ordered any families living on their boats to evacuate. Here you can see a family carrying clothing and bedding from their cabin cruiser onto the pier. The mood has changed since yesterday, when people were merely glum. This evening there is real anger at Shilshole Bay. Nick Remick for Channel Five."

"This is Basil Smithfield. I'm down here on the central waterfront, where I've been talking with the man in the little yellow and orange building where tourists buy their tickets for harbor tours and the boat trip to Tillicum Village. He tells me that few people are buying, and it's easy to understand. The beaches of Blake Island are plastered in crude oil, and people's curiosity to see what Elliott Bay looks like full of oil is rapidly wearing off. Merchants and restaurant owners along the waterfront are worried about business. Eating shrimp and crackers under the orange and white umbrellas of the Sourdough may be out of fashion for a while. Although double booms like you see here have kept the oil out of most spaces between the piers, the aroma over this whole area is not likely to give you an appetite. It seems to have driven people away from the waterfront park; the public fishing pier is deserted, and this large sign warns, 'Fish at Your Own Risk.' The gulls still circle overhead, and the ferry whistles still sound, but it's a mournful summer day on the Seattle waterfront.

"Basil Smithfield for Channel Four."

"This is Mary Kelly for Channel Seven. I'm out here

on the beach near Alki Point, where Seattle's first settlers came ashore way back in 1851, and I think it's fair to say that if the beach had looked then the way it looks now, those first men and women of Seattle would never have gotten off the ship."

10

The President of the United States arrived at Boeing Field in bright summer sunshine. About 200 people, many carrying placards, watched as the President, accompanied by aides, newsmen, and his striking, blonde wife, descended the steps of the silver and blue Presidential jet to be greeted by Senator Larsen, Mayor Rahm, and Coast Guard Commander Newhart. The President waved a few times to the crowd, ignored the chants of "Get the tankers out!" and was whisked off to the waiting Navy helicopter which would carry him and his party over the spill area.

The crowd broke up quickly, some disappointed that the President had not spoken to them. He would be making a statement later after he had toured the scene, but they had hoped for some words or some sign. They would have to wait. Reporters filed their stories for the noon news describing the intensive security precautions at the airport. Placards were stuffed into the trunks of cars, and the cars headed north on Interstate 5. Within minutes nothing marked the scene at Boeing Field but the litter of fallen leaflets announcing an anti-oil rally the next day at the federal courthouse.

The President was soon airborne over Elliott Bay. From high above the normally blue water the oil could be seen spread out in all directions like a viscous infection. Cleanup vessels were specks of flotsam in a muddy sea; the ferryboats were children's toys. Mayor Rahm, leaning forward, directed the President's attention to various landmarks below.

The pool newsmen, squeezed into the rear seats, could not hear much of what was being said against the din of the helicopter's egg-beating blades, but they could see the President shaking his head. To the west the Olympic Mountains were etched sharply against the blue sky, but all kept their eyes on the scene below as if it would not be proper to enjoy the pristine beauty of the Olympic skyline. The First Lady trained her binoculars on Wing Point, shook her head, then handed the binoculars to Senator Larsen. The President began making notes on the back of an envelope.

Off West Point the Senator called the President's attention to the site where the *Grand Canyon* had cracked open and spilled her cargo into the sea. The helicopter dropped down over Shilshole Bay, the largest marina affected by the spill, where over a thousand boats raised masts skyward in salute, then whirred on a low course for Golden Gardens. Cleanup volunteers on the beach paid scant attention. There was nothing uncommon about surveillance helicopter flights over the scene. One elderly woman, resting for a moment against a sun-bleached log, put a hand up to shade her eyes and saw the helicopter turn north and become a small speck against the cloudless sky.

The helicopter was seen off False Bay on south San Juan Island where thick, black sludge covered the shores. It was seen by the residents of the few scattered homes and cottages on the cliffs above Eagle Cove; it was seen gliding slowly over the tractors bulldozing the surface of South Beach; it was seen passing along the shores of Griffin Bay and circling over Friday Harbor; it was seen by a farmer near Davis Bay on south Lopez; a woman coming out of Richardson's General Store saw it swoop over the rocky inlets to the north. MacKaye Harbor, Barlow Bay and every cove and cliff from Iceberg Point to Cape St. Mary—the President of the United States saw it all before the Navy helicopter, turning off at a forty-five-degree angle, flew him directly over Bird Rocks, circled twice and then went on over Cypress Island's Secret Harbor to the northernmost tip of Guemes Island. There, the rocky beach around Clark Point was completely drowned in black muck. Below the beach bluff covered with shrubs and wildflowers, a few islanders sat and stared disconsolately at the uncleanable black rocks. The racket of the approaching helicopter provided an oddly welcome excuse to look up into the clean blue sky. Someone wondered aloud if that was the President. Everyone knew he was in the area today, somewhere. What would he think? What would he say? And what would happen after that? Would it make any difference? The helicopter headed north toward Lummi Bay.

Ernie Penn had only half an hour's notice that the President was coming to inspect the ruined Lummi project. The Lummis would have a chance to voice their anger and despair; the President would see it for himself, but what more would come of it Penn did not know.

At this point he had little confidence and less hope that it would make any difference. He and the rest of the waiting delegation stood quietly as the sputtering machine dropped from the sky.

The President and his party emerged and shook hands all around. Penn led the way from the oyster hatchery to the shore of the foul-smelling pond where the Lummis' hopes had died. A small child was there throwing rocks in the water.

"What would your fish and oysters have been worth if they had been able to mature for market?" the President asked.

"The fish in the pond were worth about three and a half million dollars. The oysters were worth about two million. We also had another million dollars in oysters seeded outside the dike."

"I have some idea of what you've been doing here," the President said. "Senator Larsen has told me about the project and what it means. I understand that it provided employment for 200 of the Lummi people, is that right?"

Ernie Penn nodded.

"And that you would need about three million dollars to get the project going again?"

Penn nodded again. "That's right," he said, "but our people will have to vote on whether or not to try."

"Well, keep Senator Larsen informed and I'll do what I can." A brief round of handshakes and the dignitaries were gone.

Airborne once more, the helicopter headed for Guemes Channel, Burrows Bay and Seattle. The President had asked to walk on the beach at Golden Gardens. The Seattle police were notified and were busily setting up the security guard. Part of the north parking lot was cleared of cars to serve as a landing pad. As the afternoon wore on, the word began to spread from Golden Gardens that the President was coming. The police roped off the grassy area in back of the beach. Cars were pouring down the curving drive from N.W. 85th Street to the park. Placards with hastily printed messages— "OFF THE TANKERS," "STOP THE OIL"—were tacked to wooden sticks.

Shortly after 3:00 P.M. the helicopter touched down, and the President emerged to be greeted by a roar of cheers and applause from the crowd that numbered in the thousands. He conferred briefly with his aides; he would address the people first, then take one last look at the shoreline.

Escorted through the crowd by Seattle police, he mounted a bare wooden platform which had been set up in the parking lot. The hot sun, the expectant crowd, the waving signs—it could have been one of his campaign stops two summers ago were it not for the oily sea in the background still lapping at the sloping margin of the shore with layers and layers of oily scum. Far down at the north end of the beach he could see two figures in rubber hip boots busy raking up oily seaweed, indifferent to politics and Presidents.

In the 1976 campaign, the major oil companies had generally supported his opponent, a man who advocated continuing or expanding financial incentives to the oil industry for increasingly risky explorations. The President, on the other hand, had refused to discuss the energy "crisis"; he would only call it the energy "problem." He said that he would not let his administration be governed by panic. His first two years in office had been dominated by the struggle to bring the nation's economy under control. During this time, while few would have called him a radical, he had shown his willingness to take on big industry by putting profits under tight controls. His ability to project personal warmth and integrity made him a popular leader. The people of Seattle who gathered at Golden Gardens expected sympathy, and they were not disappointed.

The President began by talking about his flight across the country from the other Washington that morning, how he had watched with the usual fascination while under him passed the prairies, the raw tips of the Rockies and the great rivers.

"From a plane," he said, "one can see all that and think of what this country was like when it was wild, before the explorers arrived and claimed it as a new world. And I have always thought of this area as being as close as any part of our country to still being a new world, fresh and clean and beautiful.

"Today," he went on, "when I was confronted with the sight of blackened beach after blackened beach, I realized once again how little time it's taking us to turn a new world into a used world, dog-eared, grimy and degraded.

"My fellow Americans, I share your heartsickness over this calamitous mess, and I'm filled with admiration for the courage and the stamina you've displayed in struggling with the spreading oil. A drama like this one has no heroes, just thousands of tired, dedicated workers.

"For some time," he continued, "my administration has been considering a proposal to designate Puget Sound as a National Marine Sanctuary." There was a

[125]

stirring in the crowd, a noticeable reaction to the President's words. "This morning I spoke with the Secretary of Commerce and instructed him to proceed with this designation as rapidly as possible. This will lead to the development of appropriate regulations to insure that the Sound will be preserved as a living body of water." Applause came rolling from the listeners in a long wave. The reality of the spilled oil was, for that moment, blotted out by hope. The President stood quietly, listening. When he spoke again his voice seemed to have more conviction.

"We must have the confidence that Puget Sound will eventually return to what it was, that it will regain its productivity and its natural beauty. But we must also be ready with all the necessary powers of the people and their governments to keep this kind of massive degradation from ever happening again." There was more and louder cheering.

The President then addressed himself to the question of why Puget Sound had not received this protection before. "I submit," he said, "that we have had a fuzzy sense of priorities. These waters are among the most biologically rich as well as the most beautiful areas that our nation possesses. A proper order of priorities would direct that they be kept safe for fish, fowl and children at play. Instead, we hear voices telling us that we have to make a choice, that we have to choose between environment and energy. That we have to choose between blackouts and blackened beaches. That an oil spill is a small price to pay for living in warm homes and driving our cars.

"I refuse to accept that choice. We need energy and we need oil, but we cannot allow those needs to dictate government policy with no regard for the consequences of supplying that energy and that oil." The President paused as the cheers came again. "Perhaps supertankers do not belong in Puget Sound." There was a loud roar of approval from the crowd. "Then why are they here?"

"Money!" shouted a voice in the throng. "Profit!" someone else yelled.

"Supertankers," the President continued, "are the least costly way to move oil. There are alternatives but they are more expensive for the oil companies and for us, the consumers. Safeguards are always more expensive in the short run. But I insist that this expense, this investment in the future of our natural environment can and must be borne by the oil companies and by our nation.

"For too long," he went on, "the government has concerned itself with providing incentives to the oil industry in the form of unreasonable profits. As you know, I have sent a bill to Congress which will replace the oil-depletion allowance with a more equitable system of incentives. But I will need your support to get that bill passed." The crowd roared its support. The President waited patiently for it to subside.

"The problem, basically, is that the government and the people have not taken control of the definition of the total energy situation. Certain industries and economic interests have been allowed to define energy problems in their own way, in ways that serve them best. This administration is committed to gaining control for all the people. You will recall that last year I asked Congress to approve legislation relating to energy conservation and the development of alternative energy sources—solar energy, wind, fusion. I appeal to you, the people of Puget Sound, for your support in these measures. And I also appeal to you not to lose confidence that our country is, if not a new world, at least a renewable one. The natural forces of wind, water and life can, if allowed, heal the wounds that we in our heedlessness have inflicted. Thank you."

He stepped down as the applause went on. The crowd was exhilarated. He had given them a great lift, but there were still some skeptics.

"Did you notice that he never came right out and said supertankers should be banned from the Sound?" Claudia Fitzsimmons asked Bill Wynette. Wynette remembered that the people of Santa Barbara had been lifted up and let down again and again by such heart-warming speeches. That was a decade ago, and drilling was going on at an even faster pace while oil continued to seep out of the ocean floor. Still, there was room for optimism. It was a different administration, one with far fewer ties to oil money.

"It's like always," Wynette said, "we'll just have to wait and see what happens."

The President was moving through the crowd, shaking hands. He stopped for a moment to chat with a group of sweaty, oil-smeared volunteers who were part of a bird-rescue team. Then he joined his wife and ducked behind the rope cordoning off the oddly empty and quiet section of beach prepared for his inspection. The last shot the TV viewers would see that night would show them from behind, slowly walking along, kicking at seaweed and gazing out over the water like any other beachcombers. Fifteen minutes later, the people climbing up the hill from Golden Gardens saw the Navy helicopter ascend and then disappear in the direction of Boeing Field.

The summer of 1978 wore on through the record-setting heat of August. The *Grand Canyon*'s hull was cut up for scrap at the Bremerton shipyard. Her bow lay at the bottom of the Sound. Her spilled cargo, thirteen million gallons of Prudhoe Bay crude, was not disposed of so easily. The oil had an enduring public presence visible on the beaches and also visible in the media, as illustrated by a sampling of letters printed that month in the "Voice of the People" column of the *Seattle Post-Intelligencer*.

From Stanwood:

"About fourteen years ago we moved here from Los Angeles to get away from the smog and the cars and to find the good life. This little town has become the center of our universe. But now, with the oil, I can't go fishing and my kids don't play on the beach. Friends write us from California and ask how bad it is. What do you say? It's hard."

From Seattle:

"Last weekend I was on the beach at Golden Gardens and ruined a good pair of shoes. Now they're only good for walking on oil. That's why I'm sending them to the state senator who wants to build a superport to accommodate even more of these big tankers.

"I'm also sending my gasoline credit card back to Octogon—in pieces. The oil companies are using superships because it saves them cash, but the saving to the consumer is negligible. The difference in the cost of bringing oil from Valdez to Seattle in a 250-thousand-ton ship or in a 25-thousand-ton small tanker is about eight tenths of a cent per gallon of oil."

From Ferndale, site of Octogon's refinery:

"I can't understand these people who seem to want to run the oil industry out of town. My husband works for Octogon, and it is the cleanest refinery he has ever worked in. Octogon took every precaution they could to transport the oil safely. Accidents are going to happen, and of course we all wish this one hadn't, but think carefully before you place the blame. Is this too big a price to pay for the good things that come to us through the oil industry: warm homes and transportation, not to mention the little things we take for granted like my kids' box of toys, my plastic hair curlers and the cap on our toothpaste tube? The state of Washington ought to be grateful for our oil industry. It's done a lot for my family, and it does a lot for everyone."

From Mercer Island:

"What about the United States Coast Guard? They've been saying for years that the Ports and Waterways Safety Act gave them the power to do whatever they had to, to protect Puget Sound. They're not saying anything now, and how do we know we're not going to get ships in here twice as big as the *Grand Canyon*? The Valdez oil terminal was built for them, and we've still got the natural deep waters. Why doesn't the Coast Guard just go ahead and ban the big ships?"

From Federal Way:

"When will America wake up? We talk about our oil crisis and our energy crisis when we ought to be talking about our spiritual crisis. We have lost our faith and we are being punished. It has all been prophesied, all this and worse. The time has come to convert to the power of the Lord."

From Bremerton:

"We've been lied to for years about our oil reserves. We've seen huge campaign contributions slow politicians down like lead shoes. We've watched Octogon and the other oil giants monopolize coal, gas and uranium supplies as well as oil and oil shale. The price of oil has risen faster than anything except oil-company profits. Why should we be surprised by this spill? The slogan 'The country that runs on oil can't afford to run short' hides a long history of exploitation and profiteering. I have an oil-company brochure explaining the benefits that oil will bring to Puget Sound Country, but I'm mailing it back to them because, after all, 'An industry that runs on propaganda can't afford to run short.' "

From Burien:

"It's time to stop fooling around. Nationalize the oil industry and let the people take charge. Even our politicians couldn't make a bigger mess."

While local feeling continued strong all summer, the national media found other catastrophes to cover. So it was by private and personal letter that many of Puget Sound's friends across the continent sought news of the continuing trauma. Barbara Jenkins, a Seattle housewife whose family summered each year on Guemes Island, wrote to a former college roommate in Michigan.

Labor Day, 1978

Dear Jean,

We are in the midst of cleaning up and getting ready to shut up the cottage for the year, but I thought I'd rest a few minutes and answer your letter. It still makes me ache that, after so many years of not being able to visit us, you finally came, and that was the year of our catastrophe. At least you left before Seattle and the whole surrounding area were hit. That was such a shock to people. They thought the tankers and the problems were all "way up north."

We don't plan to come back to Guemes on the weekends this fall and winter. It's a pity, because September and October can be just beautiful. But we've had all we can take of the beaches, still black, still so empty of life. Small slicks of crude oil keep washing ashore, and going wading or swimming means getting an oily film on your skin or your hair.

Speaking of oily film, you can imagine how the people in Anacortes felt a few days ago when a high-pressure relief valve on a storage tank at a refinery popped open and released a fine mist of oil that settled over everything in the city: houses and cars and streets. Just the day before, they learned that somebody's mistake in choosing disposal sites for the oily straw from the cleanup operations caused the contamination of water supplies needed for livestock and irrigation in a near-by rural area.

You asked me if there is anything new on the super-tanker moratorium passed by the legislature at the end of July. I imagine you've read in the national press that the oil companies went right to court to get an injunction against it. The final court proceedings won't get under way for some months, so the big ships are still coming in. It seems incredible to me. If nothing else, our disaster will make a lot of lawyers rich. So many individual and class-action lawsuits have been filed that it will be years before they're all settled. The newspapers are saying that cleanup costs for the spill are in the range of ten to fifteen million dollars.

And you wanted to know more about the law which the President said he would use to save our very special part of the country from further degradation. It's called the Marine Protection, Research and Sanctuaries Act, and it was passed by Congress in 1972. Under this law the Secretary of Commerce can, after consulting with federal departments, and with the approval of the President, designate as marine sanctuaries areas that he considers worthy of preserving for their conservation, recreational, ecological or aesthetic values.

Once a marine sanctuary is established, the Secretary of Commerce has the authority to control any relevant activities there so that the preservation or restoration which is the purpose of the act does, in fact, occur. The governor of the state whose territorial waters are affected has an absolute veto over the sanctuary designation, but Governor Newman seems to be with us. His transformation, whether personal or political, has been interesting to watch.

The real battle here will be around defining what constitute what the Act calls "necessary and reasonable" regulations. We expect the oil companies to go to court against the federal government on this, just as they've gone to court against the state on the moratorium. So you can see how uncertain things are at the moment. A lot of people are feeling very frustrated for that reason.

What really gets to us is the rumor that the oil companies are about to announce plans for a new oil pipeline across Canada, using the very same corridor as the present pipeline which carries natural gas from the Prudhoe Bay oilfields to the Midwest. This is the route that many conservationists advocated all along for Prudhoe Bay oil, and if it had been used from the beginning we might never have had to go through all this. Puget Sound would have received its crude oil through an overland pipeline spur from the main line, the same spur that has been bringing us most of our crude oil since the 1950's from the Alberta fields.

A few years back when Canada began to watch its oil exports to the United States more closely, the oil companies told us that we had to have Alaskan oil by ship, that we couldn't rely on foreign oil and all that. But the Transmountain Pipeline could have brought in American oil from Prudhoe Bay, with no reason to worry about Canadian export policy.

All that's happened may be sending Senator Davidson's star into eclipse. People know how hard he worked to get the legislation that authorized the Alaska pipeline through Congress. Once upon a time they were grateful. Now it's the reverse.

I dug up an article the other day that I'd saved because it shows so well how the operations of the international oil industry threaten not only our way of life here in Puget Sound, but places all around the world. One of those places is Venice.

If you remember, Venice is an island in a lagoon protected from the sea by the coastal strip known as the Lido. Behind Venice on the mainland are industrial suburbs not unlike Gary, Indiana or Linden, New Jersey. Petroleum-refining facilities discharge into the air acids and corrosive gases that are eating away the stones of Venice's lovely churches and palaces. But air pollution, as bad as it is, is not the main threat.

The most serious problem for Venice, more serious than the widely publicized "sinking into the sea" caused by drilling for industrial water supplies, is that there are several entrances through the Lido into the lagoon for the large ships to reach the refineries on the mainland. As tankers have gotten bigger, these entrances have been enlarged, and now the tides that move through these larger entrances are assaulting Venice with such force that chunks of masonry are falling from churches and palazzi into the canals. The presbytery of one beautiful church that we visited four years ago has been roped off. The roof may cave in at any moment.

It is interesting how much the situation in Venice seems to parallel our own. Unionized workers in the industrial suburbs on the mainland worry about restrictions that will inhibit the growth of those industrial areas whose biggest industry is oil refining and petrochemicals. They are thinking about jobs. Yet the refineries are highly automated operations, becoming more automated all the time, and many of the jobs that result from growth will go to outside people with special skills or company seniority. And the number of people who earn their living from the Venetian tourist industry is much larger than the number in petroleum-related jobs.

There are alternatives to the destruction of Venice, but they are not being explored: limitations on ship size, unloading outside the Lido with pipelines running to shore, diversion of tankers to other areas less precious to Western civilization. The way things are going, some people give Venice only another thirty years before the undermined foundations give way and the beautifully restored frescoes and everything else go tumbling into the sea. I'll send you a copy of the article, which was by Robert M. Adams in *The New York Review of Books*.

I was discussing these things with Tom the other day. He's back from his first year at college enormously influenced by reading Aldo Leopold. Tom says that we will never solve our pollution problems until our culture experiences a widespread change of consciousness, until we learn to "think like a mountain," to identify with the beauty and complexity of the natural world to such an extent that cost-benefit analysis applied to issues like supertankers in Puget Sound becomes, as Leopold would put it, sophisticated subterfuge.

Mike disagrees with Tom and likes to argue that it's far better to go to a public official with a good cost-benefit analysis in hand than with a religious message about the natural world. Tom says that if that's true, it's only because most public officials have so little ecological education. I listen to them both and agree with much of what they both say, but when I sit by the water on a quiet summer evening, watching the pink clouds and the barn swallows, I feel in my bones that Tom is right. It's hard for me to leave the future of so much that is dear to me to hard-headed business judgments.

By the way, have you read what it was that caused the *Grand Canyon* to go out of control? It was brought out at the Coast Guard inquiry that the seal on the hydraulic ram that turns the ship's rudder had failed. The hydraulic fluid, instead of activating the piston, just leaked out the sides. I think the same sort of thing once happened to our car. Captain Brown, the pilot, was, of course, completely cleared of all blame. And the big fishing net that was tangled up on the propeller had nothing whatever to do with the grounding.

We'll never be able to say what really was the cause. Was it a careless welding job by some workman in an East Coast factory, worrying about money or family problems? Or was it the failure of most of us to pay enough attention to these tankers to follow what was going on? You know the old nursery rhyme about the kingdom lost for want of a horseshoe nail. We have lost our kingdom, at least temporarily, but I don't believe it was really because of a broken seal.

Well, I had better go call Mike and the kids for some lunch. Mike has almost finished repainting the boat. The stuff we used to get the oil off took the paint off, too. You don't get crude oil off with soap and water. At least we were luckier than the people in the cottage next door; they had just finished repainting their boat two days before the spill.

We are so relieved that Mary seems to be coming out

of that horrible phase she was going through with birds. For several weeks after she saw the birds dying on the beach she would start to cry whenever she saw any bird, even a healthy robin. We have talked to her a lot about it, but she is too young to understand.

My love to you and Jack and the children.

Please write soon,
Barbara

P.S. The state has just announced very tight new restrictions on clam digging on beaches around the Sound that were not hit by the two spills. It seems that the closing of so many beaches that were hit put too much pressure on those that were left, and the healthy clam beds were being wiped out.

July 1, 1979

At dawn, the sloop *Curlew* sailed out to Bird Rocks and drifted near by while two of her crew placed a permanent marker at the top of the highest rock. Throughout Puget Sound, today had been declared a special Remembrance Day marking the first anniversary of the largest oil spill in United States history.

The old signs proclaiming Bird Rocks a National Wildlife Refuge were still there, but some things had changed. The green band of grasses and tough shrubs that had formerly brightened the craggy surface of the middle rock was gone. Now the rocks were ringed like a bathtub with layers of black scum that had become as hard as asphalt. Like other isolated outcroppings in the San Juans, the rocks had not been cleaned, but left to wind and weather. A few gulls had returned to perch among the rusty shell casings, but there was no sign of the cormorants and harlequin ducks that had made the refuge home.

Among the crew of the *Curlew* as it drifted next to the desolated site of the *Grand Canyon*'s grounding was Kay Libby. For the past year she had been active in the movement to ban supertankers from Puget Sound, a movement which now had widespread citizen support. Even the tourist industry had gotten involved. The new and militant Puget Sound Tourist Industries Council took on the oil companies at every opportunity. Fishermen, civic groups, yachtsmen, government leaders—all were part of a new alliance joined in one credo: "The *Grand Canyon*—never again."

But how to insure that it would never happen again? The tankers were still coming in. Octo's legal challenge to the state's moratorium was still in the courts. A decision was expected within weeks from the United States District Court in Seattle. That decision, whatever it was, was sure to be appealed. Minor spills were still occurring on a regular basis. And in May, a Liberian flagship bringing oil into a refinery at Anacortes had hit an outbound log ship in the fog off Neah Bay. Four thousand barrels of oil were spilled.

Shortly after that, a small armada of Seattleites, including Kay Libby, had taken their sailboats out to the entrance to the Straits to "blockade" the *Grand Canyon*'s sister ship, the *Eastern Seaboard*, inbound for the Octo refinery. The sailboats spaced themselves to avoid being hit by the tanker. She could not have stopped in time even had she wanted to. And she did not want to. It was still business as usual for the tankers on Puget Sound.

The gulls cried and circled overhead as the *Curlew* turned her nose from Bird Rocks and sailed shoreward.

As the day wore on, other ceremonies took place. At Deception Pass Park, at 9:00 A.M., two dozen people came through the picnic ground, formed a circle on the beach, and held a religious service in memory of dead fish, birds, crabs and other creatures. A small noon gathering assembled in front of the county courthouse in Friday Habor. In Seattle, a mass rally was held at 3:00 P.M. on the downtown waterfront, and those attending were asked not to come by car. The request was honored; people biked in, hiked in or took the bus.

At Peace Arch Park, near Blaine, a large crowd of Americans and Canadians assembled to express their opposition to continued tanker traffic. Governor Newman of Washington spoke first, outlining the costs in millions of dollars that the people of his state had sustained. State expenses for cleanup—five million dollars' worth—had been paid back by Octo. But the losses to the fishing and tourist industries, as well as many other costs, still awaited difficult court decisions.

"I think we can recognize now," the governor said, "that there is no adequate reimbursement for a spill on the scale that we saw last year. We could be in court for twenty years trying to establish the exact amount of damage, in dollar value, that could be attributed to the oil. The time has come to say that whatever the benefits of oil traffic, the risks are too great; we won't endure them." Claudia Fitzsimmons, on her last assignment before taking a new job with the *Washington Post*, remembered 1973, when Newman, then a state senator, had voted against a barrel tax on oil.

Another speaker was Bill Wynette. He seemed to be in a somber mood. "I can't help thinking," he said, "that even if the courts rule in our favor in the next few weeks, or the Supreme Court rules in our favor in coming months, we will still have tanker traffic on Puget Sound and we will still have oil spills. In fact, we will be about where we were in 1971, before supertankers starting coming in. But today, when the natural world becomes less recognizable every year, merely holding the fort is a victory. For us, 'the more things stay the same, the more they've changed.' "

Then, as if reluctant to end on too much of a downbeat, Wynette said that he wanted to read a few words sent to the gathering by Evelyn Stilwell, director of the British Columbia Environmental Council.

Wynette called the attention of the crowd to the phrase at the top of the Peace Arch: "Children of a Common Mother." "Those words," he said, "have always been indicative of a special relationship between the citizens of Canada and the United States. But I think their original sense is narrow and out of date. We are generations removed from that political bond.

"Yet there is something we all have in common," he went on, "another mother with whom all of us here can claim kinship, whatever our citizenship or ethnic origin." He pointed westward, toward the sea. "The ocean, eons ago the mother of us all, still is more important to us than we know, and especially to those of us who live on the banks of one of the most productive estuaries in the world. We should never forget our geography, the sense of our place between the mountains and the ocean, that makes the Pacific Northwest like no other place. If we can find unity in that, the political barriers fade into the background."

Those unable to attend a rally could, if they chose, take part in the day simply by turning on their radios or television sets. Puget Sound stations were devoting most of their programming to the *Grand Canyon* spill and its effects.

Channel Five's coverage started with the premiere showing of an hour-long documentary called "The Day Puget Sound Died." Shots of Guemes Channel, Cattle Point and Elliott Bay recreated the hot, hellish weeks of strewing and raking straw, the cries of dying grebes, the back-and-forth maneuvering of tugs and booms.

Then the film's footage switched to more recent days. Thomas Hatcher, clipboard and bucket in hand, was shown examining a square foot of gravelly beach. "We have watched this beach closely all year," he said to an interviewer. "Here below the high-tide line you see that there is little visible evidence of the spill, even though this was a very hard-hit area. Winter storms and the sheer energy of the beach—the constantly shifting gravel and pebbles—have buried and diffused the oily residue. But though the beach looks clean, we are finding oil in the local clams and crabs. So the state health people have now had to close this beach to clamming for the second year in a row. The same is true of nearly all other beaches that were hit." Hatcher was asked to comment on the biological study produced by Octo's four-person research team. "I wish I could," he said, "but none of their data is being made public."

Captain Brown had granted Channel Five a rare interview from his home on Magnolia Bluff. He recalled the moments before grounding. "After we turned to avoid the fishing boats, I ordered a correction to straighten our course. I had my back to DeNunzio, the quartermaster, and when nothing happened I felt slightly irritated. I said, 'De Nunzio, did you hear me?' I turned around and he was white as a sheet. 'Captain, she's not answering,' he said. I'll never forget those next few moments. I knew where we were, and I could picture Bird Rocks coming up on us. There was no way to stop in time. There was no way to turn, there was no way to do anything."

Channel Five talked to Oran Jensen, still an oil-spill supervisor with the Department of Ecology. Jensen recalled his panic in the early morning of July 2 when a phone call, rousing him from sleep, put him in charge of a nightmare. "When I flew over Bird Rocks that morning and got my first glimpse of that ship on the rocks with oil all around her," he said, "I had the feeling in the pit of my stomach that everything was out of control. That exact feeling comes back to me from time to time when I realize that the same thing could happen again tomorrow. The phone could ring and I could wake up to the same picture."

"He's not the only one," thought Russell Lindstrom, watching the program over a beer in the Harbor House. He remembered sitting out week after week of the 1978 sockeye runs. The fishermen had lost at least five million dollars. Losses to the canneries, retailers and others who derived secondary income from salmon had never been computed. Crab fishing had been wiped out for the year by Washington Health Department restrictions on sales. So fishermen who ordinarily relied on crabbing to eke out the winter had lined up at the unemployment office. It had been a sad year.

This summer the sockeye season had been open for five days. There was more than the usual amount of excitement and hope for a good run of sockeye, because the runs of pink salmon were expected to be poor. The pinks, or humpbacks, had a two-year cycle. Last year, the newly-spawned fry had been feeding all through the Gulf and San Juan islands and slowly proceeding seaward when the oil spill hit. Thousands of three-inch fingerlings had washed up dead on San Juan beaches, but since dead salmon tend to sink rather than float, no one really knew how many had died. Divers sent down in selected areas during the first few days after the spill had found many dead fish on the sea bottom. It looked bad for the pinks.

The Fraser River sockeye moving out to sea in 1978 were on a four-year cycle. The International Pacific Salmon Fisheries Commission hoped that most of the sockeye had completed their migration out to the Pacific through Juan de Fuca Strait before the oil hit. But because so many dead sockeye smolts had been found on San Juan beaches, there was considerable apprehension. No one would know until 1981 what damage had been done. Would the sockeye be coming back to spawn, or wouldn't they?

Russell Lindstrom preferred not to think about it. Turning his back on the steady stream of reminiscing that was coming over the tube, he went home to get a little sleep before beginning the long night of the gillnetter.

In Victoria, Cecil Cory waited to tee off at his golf club. He too was contemplating the past year. Anti-American sentiment had run high among the people of British Columbia, but there was also discontent with Ottawa.

In 1973, officials of the Canadian Government had offered the Puget Sound region all the crude oil it would need by pipeline from Alberta if supertanker traffic into Juan de Fuca Strait could be banned. The Nixon Administration had refused. Interior Secretary Morton claimed that Canada would merely be diverting oil needed by the Midwest.

Now British Columbians were pressuring their federal government to renew the offer—but with little success. Canada's transcontinental pipeline system had recently been extended from Toronto to Montreal, and Alberta oil was moving east to feed Quebec and the Maritime Provinces. The fears of British Columbians had to be balanced against the oil needs of eastern Canada, traditionally dependent on overseas imports.

Cory, for his part, did not get involved in the politics of it. His job was to be ready for the next accident. The effects of the *Grand Canyon* spill, he thought, had been a little exaggerated by the conservationists. It was true that there had been more biological damage than he had anticipated. In the future he would be more sparing with the use of chalk and sand to sink oil, because studies showed that it was staying at the bottom in clumps that were still releasing poisons a year later.

There could be much worse catastrophes, Cory felt. In only a few coves around Victoria could traces of the oil still be seen. And yet—something jogged at his soul. For three months it had been a bloody mess. All that work trying to keep the oil out, most of it futile. Cory felt a sudden sharp desire for the day when Puget Sound might stop paying so steep a price to the industrial era.

At Cherry Point, a faint smell of sulfur hung over the Octo refinery as it cracked out its usual 125 thousand barrels a day. It was no special day here, except for the presence of Bill Berry and Lambert Bibb working together in one of the administrative offices on a Sunday.

Berry was tired. It had been a year of bad press for Octo in the Northwest. As the public-relations man for the refinery he had taken a lot of flak. He and Bibb, who had come up again from Los Angeles, had just spent an intensive week mounting a publicity campaign of ads and press releases in the local media to counter the anti-oil sentiment inevitably building up around the July 1 anniversary. Berry did not say anything to Bibb, but he was thinking of looking for a new job.

North of Bellingham at Lummi Bay, nothing at all was happening. The aquaculture buildings had been nailed shut and "No Trespassing" signs put up. No one was about. Ernie Penn was in Olympia working for the Washington Department of Fisheries. Of the other 200 former employees of the aquaculture project, a few were fishing, a few had found other jobs, many were unemployed. Although the President and Washington's two senators had given assurances of a three-million-dollar grant of operating capital to get the project started again, Ernie Penn and most of the other members of the Lummi tribe considered it a waste of time until the tanker question was settled once and for all.

In a furnished room on Seattle's Queen Anne Hill, the *Grand Canyon*'s chief engineer sat studying the Olympics through his telescope. The telescope was the only extraneous item in a space otherwise as spare and neat as ship's quarters. The chief engineer spent as little time here as possible; he loved to be at sea. But not on tankers any more. The events of the night of July 1, 1978, were unnerving enough as he relived them in his imagination, without taking the risk of having them happen again. He now had a berth as chief engineer with a cargo ship. It would be leaving for Australia tomorrow.

Through the telescope, the chief engineer watched the shadows lengthen on the snowy east side of Mount Constance. Evening was approaching. He opened his Bible and found a favorite passage in Jeremiah: "And I brought you into a plentiful country, to eat the fruit thereof and the goodness thereof; But when ye entered, ye defiled my land, and made mine heritage an abomination."

Over Seattle, the sky was turning scarlet and violet at the horizon, below the luminous clouds. The rally at the waterfront had long since ended. Now there was just the usual bustle, with the comings and goings of the ferries, and people on their way to dinner or taking a walk. Next to the fountain at the ferry terminal stood a newly erected concrete pedestal bearing a bizarre monument: a twisted and crumpled slab of black metal. An out-of-town passerby, idly curious as to its meaning, stopped to read the inscription and learned that it was a chunk of the hull of a sunken tanker. The inscription read:

On July 1, 1978, the tanker *Grand Canyon* ran aground on Bird Rocks in Rosario Strait. Eight million gallons of crude oil escaped into Puget Sound. On July 13, 1978, while the wrecked vessel was being towed to the Bremerton shipyard, she broke in two and lost another five million gallons.

The damage done to Puget Sound cannot be measured merely in dollars. The fouled beaches, the dead fish and birds, the diseased waters exacted from the human community a toll of spirit as well.

This was a disaster that need not have happened. That it did happen can be atoned for only by a new recognition: that in losing this pure, fruitful body of water we lose our own souls; but that by sustaining it we can sustain ourselves. To that end this monument is dedicated.

PUGET SOUND: LIVE ON IN PEACE.

APPENDIX

Risk Analysis of the Oil Transportation System. A Report to the 43rd Legislature, State of Washington, by the Oceanographic Institute of Washington, 1973:

Bringing crude oil into Puget Sound is not a new problem. . . . The immediate concern is with the increased size of tankers transporting oil on Washington waters and the hazards involved. There is considerably more difficulty maneuvering these large tankers; their stopping distances can be measured in miles; and the quantity of crude oil that can be spilled is staggering (a grounding resulting in the rupture of one main or two wing tanks could release over 4,000,000 gallons of oil from a modern 120,000 dwt tanker).

West Coast Deepwater Port Facilities Study. U.S. Army Corps of Engineers, June, 1973:

Until recently, the Nisseki Maru, at 372,000 dwt, held the world record for the largest tanker in service. Now, the Globtik Tokyo, a 477,000 dwt tanker, has entered world service. Since January 1971, the U.S. Maritime Administration [estimates] that over 275 tankers in the 250,000-300,000 dwt class have been either under construction or placed on order. The growth in larger ships is expected to continue in the foreseeable future. Vessels in the 250,000-300,000 dwt class now number in the hundreds. By 1980, the Maritime Administration estimates their number will be in the thousands.

Risk Analysis of the Oil Transportation System:

It appears inevitable that the Puget Sound area with its naturally deep harbors will become one of the nation's super seaports. Survey work has been started at Cherry Point for possible development of a 90-foot ship navigation channel which could handle the world's largest tankers, according to a NOAA report.

Risk Analysis of the Oil Transportation System:

A detailed study of collision and grounding should be pursued in the pathway which transits Rosario Strait. The entrances (south end bounded by Bell Rocks, Pt. Colville and Davidson Rocks, and the north end between Clark Island, The Sisters and Village Point on Lummi Island) are especially hazardous for meeting situations and leave restricted space for maneuvering. The numerous rocks and shoals also present hazards from grounding.

West Coast Deepwater Port Facilities Study:

Two refineries . . . are located at Ferndale . . . . Standard Oil of California owns land in the area as does Glacier Park Co., a subsidiary of Burlington Northern Railroad and Puget Power. Thus facilities either exist, or the potential is there for expansion, to handle deep port traffic, large amounts of crude oil and supporting facilities.

West Coast Deepwater Port Facilities Study:

The State of Washington Department of Natural Resources has considered Ferndale in terms of an expanded deepwater port facility and finds that severe currents and seastates experienced in the Straits of Rosario and the more exposed waters north thereof, make Ferndale a problem site from the standpoint of spill control. The aquaculture project and shellfish culture areas, . . . as well as the intensively used public recreation areas in and around the San Juan Islands, are major resources cited at risk in connection with siting at Ferndale.

Oil on Puget Sound: An Interdisciplinary Study in Systems Engineering. Directed by Juris Vagners and co-ordinated by Paul Mar, University of Washington Press, 1972:

The expected number of oil spills in Puget Sound over the next ten years, 1970-1980, resulting from a vessel collision [only] is predicted to range from a low of 0.67 to a high of

2.69 vessel collisions. For the period 1980-1990 the corresponding values are 1.07 and 3.56.

West Coast Deepwater Port Facilities Study:

An oil spill in the approaches to the San Juan Islands could disperse throughout the archipelago with long-term effects.

West Coast Deepwater Port Facilities Study:

Impacts of a major oil spill . . . would not necessarily be limited to the disruption of the natural environment, but could result in severe economic damage to the fisheries, shellfish, and recreation industry.

Oil on Puget Sound:

Without a doubt, the Puget Sound region is one of the richest fishing grounds in the nation and for that consideration alone, prime importance must be given to the national and international responsibility of the local citizenry to preserve such a resource.

Environmental Assessment, West Coast Deepwater Port Study. Battelle Pacific Northwest Laboratories, June, 1973:

The relatively undisturbed and undeveloped nature of much of the Puget Sound country is a major asset in terms of tourism . . . this area has few rivals in the world. Expenditures by tourists are a dependable and important contribution to the economy.

Oil on Puget Sound:

The biological resources within Puget Sound represent one of the most, if not the most, important resources of the State of Washington. Abundant and varied forms of life are present. Crabs, clams, oysters, five species of salmon, and many species of bottom fish are important economically. A great deal of recreation is derived from these and other

[155]

organisms. Destruction or elimination of any of these resources would represent a severe blow to the quality of life of the citizens of Washington.

The Honorable Bert Cole, State Commissioner of Public Lands, at a U.S. Senate Commerce Committee hearing, July, 1971:

I am firmly convinced that, in combination with recreation, the long range economic role for the waters . . . of Puget Sound lies in the area of aquaculture. Besides its potentially considerable economic plusses, aquaculture represents an environmentally appropriate utilization of our renewable resources.

The Honorable Warren G. Magnuson, Chairman, U.S. Senate Commerce Committee, hearing, July, 1971:

We may eventually employ as many people in the oceanographic field—a field totally compatible with the resources and environment of the Pacific Northwest—as we have employed in the aerospace industry. . . . Threats to the Puget Sound environment are threats to our aspirations for making Puget Sound an oceanic center. That is why I have repeatedly said that we cannot tolerate oil spills of any kind.

Oil on Puget Sound:

The standard answer for what should be done about oil spill control today is to entrust it to technology. Supposedly, this mystical word will permit industry to extract 20,000 barrels of oil from Puget Sound waters when a cargo tank of a large tanker is split open from grounding or collision. In spite of the many advances in oil spill recovery techniques, the resources at command are pitifully ineffective when compared to the requirement dictated by a spill of any significant size.

Risk Analysis of the Oil Transportation System:

We recommend that the legislature provide the Oceanographic Commission of Washington with funding to determine the technical, economic and environmental feasibility of transporting petroleum products to and from oil refineries in the State of Washington by pipeline and other alternatives to waterborne vessels.

OFFICE OF THE MAYOR • CITY OF SEATTLE

WES UHLMAN   MAYOR

June 25, 1973

Lt. Col. Frederick Mueller
Corps of Engineers
Pier 36
Seattle, Washington   98134

Dear Colonel Mueller:

As a part of your study of West Coast Deepwater Port Facilities, you have requested comments regarding various potential sites for facilities to accommodate large petroleum-carrying ships (supertankers). I am pleased to forward to you my thoughts and comments on this issue.

During the last three years, Seattle has experienced rates of unemployment much higher than the national average. In large part this was due to our dependence on the Boeing Company as the largest single employer in the area. It is well accepted that in order to prevent recurring periods of economic fluctuations, we must diversify our economic base. I have therefore initiated and cooperated with several efforts designed to accomplish these goals. Collectively, they have added millions of dollars to the local economy and created hundreds of jobs. Industrial diversification, however, must not be pursued blindly. Each case must be carefully evaluated on its applicability for this area.

The overall benefits of major petrochemical activity in or around Puget Sound to the people of Seattle appear insubstantial. Petroleum refining is capital intensive, bringing very little new, permanent employment to the area. (In fact, each year *Fortune Magazine* reports the petroleum industry as having both the highest capital assets per employee ratio and the highest rate of sales per employees.)

It will be argued that the existence of a refinery center on Puget Sound will assure the region of adequate petroleum supplies in any future period of shortage. I believe this is a false hope. In all probability the Congress will act to regulate such allocations during any long term fuel shortage.

On the other hand, the potential and very real environmental dangers are extremely troublesome. The development of a petroleum superport and the increase in oil traffic, oil processing, and petrochemical industries that would result will inevitably bring increased air and water pollution, increased demands for fresh water and sharply increased demands for waterfront property for industrial use. Each of these demands will have a deleterious effect on the quality of life in this region.

Tourism and fishing, both critically important industries to this area, are critically dependent on high water quality. Any decline in water quality will be destructive to these industries and cripple our plans for economic diversification.

Any increase in employment due to regional expansion of petroleum and petrochemical activity would, no doubt, be more than offset by the displacement of employment from these and similar activities.

[158]

Nature has blessed us with an environment unparalleled in this country and perhaps in the world. As custodians of this resource, we must be careful not to destroy nature's gift while trying to solve man's problems.

Sincerely,

Wes Uhlman
Mayor

WU:lpg

ACKNOWLEDGMENTS

For many different kinds of help making this book possible, we wish to warmly thank all of the following:

David A. Anderson; Malcolm Anderson; Dorothy Bird; Reade Brown, Washington Department of Game; Ben Cain; Robert C. Clark, Jr., National Marine Fisheries Service; Dr. Margaret Davies; Captain R. Deschamps, Puget Sound Pilots; Alyn C. Duxbury, Department of Oceanography, University of Washington; Robert F. Gay; Get Oil Out, Inc.; Dr. Wallace G. Heath, Lummi Aquaculture Project; Dale R. Jones; Willy Jones, Lummi Aquaculture Project; Greg Kirsch; Dennis R. Kuntz; John D. LaFarge; Dr. Robert S. Leighton; Sara Levant; Robert Lynette; Emily C. Mandelbaum; Carl Nyblade; Russell F. Orrell, Washington Department of Fisheries; Carolyn B. Phillips; Norman Sigsworth, Marine Services, Ministry of Transport, Vancouver, B.C.; Richard L. Storch, naval architect; Nora Strate; Joan Thomas; Charles M. Thorne; Herbert H. Webber, Huxley College of Environmental Studies.

Our greatest debt of all is to our editor and publisher, Dan Levant, whose interest and active collaboration with us helped shape this book and brought it into existence.

Our story is fiction rooted in fact. It is therefore appropriate to note that any remaining errors are our own.

P.C.

M.K.B.

Seattle, Washington
April, 1974

[161]